Curriculum Units

Sorting and Surveys

Data Analysis

UNIT 7

GRADE K

Infinity Prime Donna Casey

"This fractal is a classic spiral, which is my favorite, and I'm always amazed at the variations and the endlessly repeating patterns that can be created out of such a primary shape." – Donna Casey

Investigations

IN NUMBER, DATA, AND SPACE®

Sorting and Surveys

Data Analysis **UNIT 7**

Editorial offices: Glenview, Illinois • Parsippany, New Jersey • New York, New York
Sales offices: Boston, Massachusetts • Duluth, Georgia
Glenview, Illinois • Coppell, Texas • Sacramento, California • Mesa, Arizona

The Investigations curriculum was developed by TERC, Cambridge, MA.

This material is based on work supported by the National Science Foundation ("NSF") under Grant No. ESI-0095450. Any opinions, findings, and conclusions or recommendations expressed in this material are those of the author(s) and do not necessarily reflect the views of the National Science Foundation.

ISBN: 0-328-27003-2

ISBN: 978-0-328-27003-3

7 8 9 10-V003-15 14 13 12 11 10 09 08

CC:N3

Co-Principal Investigators

Susan Jo Russell

Karen Economopoulos

Authors

Lucy Wittenberg
Director Grades 3–5

Karen Economopoulos
Director Grades K–2

Virginia Bastable
(SummerMath for Teachers, Mt. Holyoke College)

Katie Hickey Bloomfield

Keith Cochran

Darrell Earnest

Arusha Hollister

Nancy Horowitz

Erin Leidl

Megan Murray

Young Oh

Beth W. Perry

Susan Jo Russell

Deborah Schifter
(Education Development Center)

Kathy Sillman

Administrative Staff

Amy Taber
Project Manager

Beth Bergeron

Lorraine Brooks

Emi Fujiwara

Contributing Authors

Denise Baumann

Jennifer DiBrienza

Hollee Freeman

Paula Hooper

Jan Mokros

Stephen Monk
(University of Washington)

Mary Beth O'Connor

Judy Storeygard

Cornelia Tierney

Elizabeth Van Cleef

Carol Wright

Technology

Jim Hammerman

Classroom Field Work

Amy Appell

Rachel E. Davis

Traci Higgins

Julia Thompson

Note: Unless otherwise noted, all contributors listed above were staff of the Education Research Collaborative at TERC during their work on the curriculum. Other affiliations during the time of development are listed.

Collaborating Teachers

This group of dedicated teachers carried out extensive field testing in their classrooms, met regularly to discuss issues of teaching and learning mathematics, provided feedback to staff, welcomed staff into their classrooms to document students' work, and contributed both suggestions and written material that has been incorporated into the curriculum.

Bethany Altchek
Linda Amaral
Kimberly Beauregard
Barbara Bernard
Nancy Buell
Rose Christiansen
Chris Colbath-Hess
Lisette Colon
Kim Cook
Frances Cooper
Kathleen Drew
Rebeka Eston Salemi
Thomas Fisher
Michael Flynn
Holly Ghazey
Susan Gillis
Danielle Harrington
Elaine Herzog
Francine Hiller
Kirsten Lee Howard
Liliana Klass
Leslie Kramer
Melissa Lee Andrichak
Kelley Lee Sadowski
Jennifer Levitan
Mary Lou LoVecchio
Kristen McEnaney
Maura McGrail
Kathe Millett
Florence Molyneaux
Amy Monkiewicz
Elizabeth Monopoli
Carol Murray
Robyn Musser
Christine Norrman
Deborah O'Brien
Timothy O'Connor
Anne Marie O'Reilly
Mark Paige
Margaret Riddle
Karen Schweitzer
Elisabeth Seyferth
Susan Smith
Debra Sorvillo
Shoshanah Starr
Janice Szymaszek
Karen Tobin
JoAnn Trauschke
Ana Vaisenstein
Yvonne Watson
Michelle Woods
Mary Wright

Advisors

Deborah Lowenberg Ball,
University of Michigan

Hyman Bass, Professor of Mathematics and Mathematics Education
University of Michigan

Mary Canner, Principal, Natick Public Schools

Thomas Carpenter, Professor of Curriculum and Instruction,
University of Wisconsin-Madison

Janis Freckmann, Elementary Mathematics Coordinator,
Milwaukee Public Schools

Lynne Godfrey, Mathematics Coach,
Cambridge Public Schools

Ginger Hanlon, Instructional Specialist in Mathematics,
New York City Public Schools

DeAnn Huinker, Director, Center for Mathematics and
Science Education Research, University of Wisconsin-Milwaukee

James Kaput, Professor of Mathematics, University of
Massachusetts-Dartmouth

Kate Kline, Associate Professor, Department of Mathematics
and Statistics, Western Michigan University

Jim Lewis, Professor of Mathematics,
University of Nebraska-Lincoln

William McCallum, Professor of Mathematics,
University of Arizona

Harriet Pollatsek, Professor of Mathematics,
Mount Holyoke College

Debra Shein-Gerson, Elementary Mathematics Specialist,
Weston Public Schools

Gary Shevell, Assistant Principal,
New York City Public Schools

Liz Sweeney, Elementary Math Department,
Boston Public Schools

Lucy West, Consultant, Metamorphosis:
Teaching Learning Communities, Inc.

This revision of the curriculum was built on the work of the many authors who contributed to the first edition (published between 1994 and 1998). We acknowledge the critical contributions of these authors in developing the content and pedagogy of *Investigations*:

Authors

Joan Akers

Michael T. Battista

Douglas H. Clements

Karen Economopoulos

Marlene Kliman

Jan Mokros

Megan Murray

Ricardo Nemirovsky

Andee Rubin

Susan Jo Russell

Cornelia Tierney

Contributing Authors

Mary Berle-Carman

Rebecca B. Corwin

Rebeka Eston

Claryce Evans

Anne Goodrow

Cliff Konold

Chris Mainhart

Sue McMillen

Jerrie Moffet

Tracy Noble

Kim O'Neil

Mark Ogonowski

Julie Sarama

Amy Shulman Weinberg

Margie Singer

Virginia Woolley

Tracey Wright

Contents

UNIT 7

Sorting and Surveys

Investigations

C U R R I C U L U M

Overview of Program Components

FOR TEACHERS

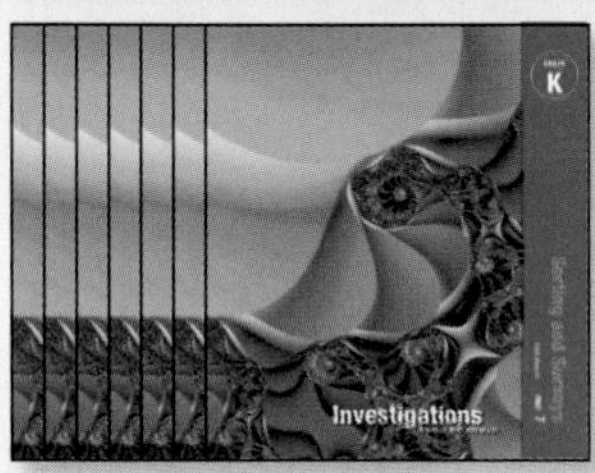

The **Curriculum Units** are the teaching guides. (See far right.)

Implementing Investigations in Kindergarten offers suggestions for implementing the curriculum. It also contains a comprehensive index.

The **Resources Binder** contains all the Resource Masters that support instruction. (Also available on CD) The binder also includes a student software CD.

FOR STUDENTS

The **Student Activity Book** contains the consumable student pages (Recording Sheets, Homework, Practice, and so on).

The **Student Math Handbook Flip Chart** contains pictures of Math Words and Ideas pages.

The *Investigations* Curriculum

Investigations in Number, Data, and Space® is a K–5 mathematics curriculum designed to engage students in making sense of mathematical ideas. Six major goals guided the development of the *Investigations in Number, Data, and Space*® curriculum. The curriculum is designed to:

- Support students to make sense of mathematics and learn that they can be mathematical thinkers
- Focus on computational fluency with whole numbers as a major goal of the elementary grades
- Provide substantive work in important areas of mathematics—rational numbers, geometry, measurement, data, and early algebra—and connections among them
- Emphasize reasoning about mathematical ideas
- Communicate mathematics content and pedagogy to teachers
- Engage the range of learners in understanding mathematics

Underlying these goals are three guiding principles that are touchstones for the *Investigations* team as we approach both students and teachers as agents of their own learning:

1. *Students have mathematical ideas.* Students come to school with ideas about numbers, shapes, measurements, patterns, and data. If given the opportunity to learn in an environment that stresses making sense of mathematics, students build on the ideas they already have and learn about new mathematics they have never encountered. Students learn that they are capable of having mathematical ideas, applying what they know to new situations, and thinking and reasoning about unfamiliar problems.

2. *Teachers are engaged in ongoing learning* about mathematics content, pedagogy, and student learning. The curriculum provides material for professional development, to be used by teachers individually or in groups, that supports teachers' continued learning as they use the curriculum over several years. The *Investigations* curriculum materials are designed as much to be a dialogue with teachers as to be a core of content for students.

3. *Teachers collaborate with the students and curriculum materials* to create the curriculum as enacted in the classroom. The only way for a good curriculum to be used well is for teachers to be active participants in implementing it. Teachers use the curriculum to maintain a clear, focused, and coherent agenda for mathematics teaching. At the same time, they observe and listen carefully to students, try to understand how they are thinking, and make teaching decisions based on these observations.

Investigations is based on experience from research and practice, including field testing that involved documentation of thousands of hours in classrooms, observations of students, input from teachers, and analysis of student work. As a result, the curriculum addresses the learning needs of real students in a wide range of classrooms and communities. The investigations are carefully designed to invite all students into mathematics—girls and boys; members of diverse cultural, ethnic, and language groups; and students with a wide variety of strengths, needs, and interests.

Based on this extensive classroom testing, the curriculum takes seriously the time students need to develop a strong conceptual foundation and skills based on that foundation. Each curriculum unit focuses on an area of content in depth, providing time for students to develop and practice ideas across a variety of activities and contexts that build on each other. Daily guidelines for time spent on class sessions, Classroom Routines (K–3), and Ten-Minute Math (3–5) reflect the commitment to devoting adequate time to mathematics in each school day.

About This Curriculum Unit

This **Curriculum Unit** is one of seven teaching guides in Grade K. The seventh unit in Grade K is *Sorting and Surveys.*

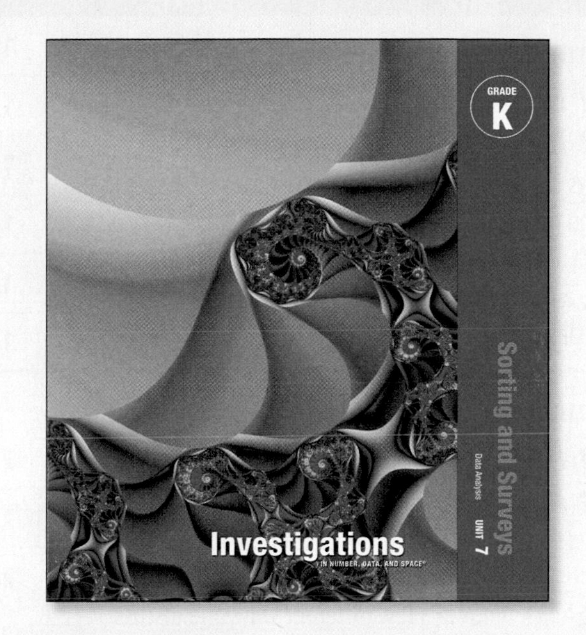

- The **Introduction and Overview** section organizes and presents the instructional materials, provides background information, and highlights important features specific to this unit.
- Each Curriculum Unit contains several **Investigations.** Each Investigation focuses on a set of related mathematical ideas.
- Investigations are divided into 30–45 minute **Sessions,** or lessons.
- Sessions have a combination of these parts: **Activity, Discussion, Math Workshop,** and **Session Follow-Up.**
- Each session also has one or more **Classroom Routines** that are done outside of math time.
- At the back of the book is a collection of **Teacher Notes** and **Dialogue Boxes** that provide professional development related to the unit.
- Also included at the back of the book are the **Student Math Handbook Flip Chart** pages for this unit.
- The **Index** provides a way to look up important words or terms.

Overview

OF THIS UNIT

<table>
<tr><th>Investigation</th><th>Session</th><th>Day</th></tr>
<tr><td rowspan="6">INVESTIGATION 1
How Many Noses? How Many Eyes?
Students count the number of people, noses, and eyes in the class and represent the data in a variety of ways. They also use data about the number of chairs and people in the class to solve a problem about whether there are enough chairs for the class.</td><td>1.1 How Many Are We?</td><td>1</td></tr>
<tr><td>1.2 How Many Noses?</td><td>2</td></tr>
<tr><td>1.3 How Many Eyes?</td><td>3</td></tr>
<tr><td>1.4 Counting Chairs</td><td>4</td></tr>
<tr><td>1.5 Eyes at Home</td><td>5</td></tr>
<tr><td>1.6 Enough Chairs for the Class?</td><td>6</td></tr>
<tr><td rowspan="6">INVESTIGATION 2
How Are They the Same? How Are They Different?
Students sort people and objects according to their attributes. They also organize a set of data about their favorite lunch foods in a few different ways and discuss what they notice about the data.</td><td>2.1 Self-Portraits</td><td>7</td></tr>
<tr><td>2.2 Attribute Match-Up</td><td>8</td></tr>
<tr><td>2.3 Boxes, Bottles, and Cans</td><td>9</td></tr>
<tr><td>2.4 Same and Different</td><td>10</td></tr>
<tr><td>2.5 Attribute Dominoes</td><td>11</td></tr>
<tr><td>2.6 Favorite Lunch Foods</td><td>12</td></tr>
<tr><td rowspan="5">INVESTIGATION 3
Data Projects
Students develop their own "Do You Like . . . ?" survey questions. They ask their classmates their survey question, record their responses, and then share their data with the rest of the class. Students also solve a problem using attendance data and discuss how they solved the problem.</td><td>3.1 "Do You Like . . . ?" Surveys</td><td>13</td></tr>
<tr><td>3.2 Collecting Data</td><td>14</td></tr>
<tr><td>3.3 Sharing "Do You Like . . . ?" Surveys</td><td>15</td></tr>
<tr><td>3.4 End-of-Unit Assessment: Solving a Problem Using Attendance Data</td><td>16</td></tr>
<tr><td>3.5 End-of-Unit Assessment and How Did You Solve the Problem?</td><td>17</td></tr>
</table>

Each *Investigations* session has some combination of these four parts: **Activity, Discussion, Math Workshop,** and **Session Follow-Up.** These session parts are indicated in the chart below. Each session also has one or more **Classroom Routines** that are done outside of math time.

					Classroom Routines			
Activity	Discussion	Math Workshop	Assessment Checklist*	Session Follow-Up	*Calendar*	*Attendance*	*Today's Question*	*Patterns on the Pocket Chart*
●●	●		●	●		●		
●	●●	●		●			●	
●●				●	●			
●	●	●	●	●				●
●	●	●		●		●		
	●	●		●			●	
●●●				●	●			
●	●	●	●	●				●
●	●	●		●		●		
	●	●		●			●	
●	●	●		●	●			
●●	●			●				●
●●	●			●		●		
	●	●		●			●	
	●	●		●	●			
●●	●			●				●
	●	●		●		●		

*An Assessment Checklist is introduced in this session.

Mathematics

IN THIS UNIT

Sorting and Surveys is the seventh of seven units in the Kindergarten sequence. Collecting, representing, and interpreting information are ongoing activities in our daily lives. In today's world, these activities are vital to understanding events and making decisions. Young students' curiosity makes them avid collectors of materials and information. Working with data builds on their desire to know about their world and the people in it. In this unit, students count, compare, sort, and represent information—each process is an important part of data analysis and of the Kindergarten mathematics curriculum.

This unit develops ideas about counting, representing data, carrying out a data investigation, sorting and classifying, and using data to solve a problem. In this unit, students sort a variety of objects according to their attributes, as well as sorting data about their favorite lunch foods. They represent numerical data about their class and carry out their own data investigation by collecting responses to their own survey questions. They also solve problems using data they have collected about their class.

This unit builds on the work with counting, sorting and classifying, and representing information that students have worked on throughout the Kindergarten curriculum.

This unit focuses on 4 Mathematical Emphases:

1 Counting and Quantity **Developing strategies for accurately counting a set of objects by ones**

Math Focus Points

- Counting and keeping track of quantities
- Matching sets with a one-to-one correspondence
- Working with two-to-one correspondence
- Counting by groups of 2

Counting is an important way for children to develop an understanding of what numbers mean. By the end of Kindergarten, students are using counting as a tool for describing their world and for solving problems. To do this, they must remember the rote-counting sequence, assign one counting number to each object counted, and have a strategy for keeping track of what has already been counted and what still needs to be counted. The expectation is that end-of-the-year kindergarteners are working on counting numbers into the twenties; those numbers that represent the total number of students in their classroom. The total number of students is a significant number, and while counting into the twenties may be challenging for some students, working with the number of students in the class, even if that number is in the twenties, will be a familiar task to most students.

When students collect data, they are counting in very real ways. Central to any data collection activity is the need to establish the group of people or objects being considered. Knowing how many are in that group encourages students to develop strategies for keeping track of who has been counted. It also reinforces the one-to-one correspondence between the number of people in the group and the total number of responses.

2 Data Analysis Representing data

Math Focus Points

- Making a representation of a set of data
- Seeing the one-to-one correspondence between a set of data and a representation of this data set

Our world is flooded with different types of graphs, charts, and data displays, all intended to communicate specific information. Students need to examine and understand different kinds of representations so they can make sense of information and become critical readers of data. They also need to communicate what they know about data through their own representations. In this unit, students build models and make representations on paper that communicate the data they have collected to others.

3 Data Analysis Sorting and classifying

Math Focus Points

- Identifying the attributes of an object
- Identifying an attribute that is common to several objects
- Comparing how objects are the same and different
- Using attributes to sort a set of objects
- Grouping data into categories based on similar attributes
- Sorting a set of objects or data in different ways

Identifying and carefully describing attributes of an object are essential to dealing with data. By examining how things are the same and different, we are able to sort things into groups and classify them on the basis of their attributes. Sorting and classifying are useful tools in all areas of mathematics. For example, being able to describe the attributes of a square and to think about how it is the same as and different from other four-sided figures helps create a definition of a square.

Sorting and classifying are central to organizing and interpreting data. As students think about how pieces of information are the same and different, they begin to form the basis for determining how data might be grouped and how those groups might be defined. While kindergarteners are not yet ready to consider many attributes at the same time, they are excellent observers; they often think about how things go together in an effort to make sense out of their world. Throughout the unit, students gain experience in describing, sorting, and defining the information they collect, and they begin to develop categorization skills by making decisions about what categories to use and which data belong in which categories.

4 Data Analysis Carrying out a data investigation

Math Focus Points

- Choosing a survey question with two possible responses
- Collecting and keeping track of survey data
- Interpreting results of a data investigation
- Using data to solve a problem

To understand the processes involved in data analysis, even young students need to be involved in all phases of conducting a survey. Kindergarteners, though true beginners in conducting surveys, need experience in this sometimes messy mathematical realm. They need to experience choosing and posing a question, deciding on how to record responses, and making sense of and counting the results.

Because all of these processes are interrelated, it is essential to experience the entire process to understand how one step leads to the next. Decisions must be made at each stage. For example, what do you do with responses that do not fit into the categories you have created? In this unit, students have the opportunity to make many of those important decisions involved in a data investigation themselves.

Adults use data in their daily lives to inform decisions and to solve problems. In this unit, students begin to use some of the data they collect to solve mathematical problems connected to their classroom. They find out how many chairs are in the class and then figure out whether there are enough chairs for students in the class. They use data about the number of students in the class and the number absent to help them figure out the number of students present that day. Students need to experience data analysis not as an isolated field of mathematics, but as connected to and useful for other mathematical topics and their own lives.

This Unit also focuses on

- Comparing two quantities to determine which is more

Classroom Routines focus on

- Developing strategies for counting accurately
- Considering whether order matters when you count
- Comparing quantities
- Counting forward and backward
- Using the calendar as a tool for keeping track of time
- Collecting, counting, representing, describing, and comparing data
- Determining what comes next in a repeating pattern
- Describing repeating patterns

In Grade 1, students continue their work on sorting and on the many aspects of data collection and analysis. They sort a variety of collections of materials including buttons, shells, and shapes and learn a game called *Guess My Rule* in which they try to guess the rule by which a group of objects have been sorted. Students in first grade have an opportunity again to do their own survey—this time creating surveys with two possible responses, collecting the data, and then creating representations to communicate to others the results to their surveys. Finally students collect numerical data about the ages of students in their class, represent this data, and compare the data to the ages of students in another class.

Assessment

IN THIS UNIT

Every session in this unit provides an opportunity for Ongoing Assessment. In addition, assessment checklists are provided to keep track of your observations about students' work with concepts and ideas that are benchmarks for this unit.

ONGOING ASSESSMENT: Observing Students at Work

The following sessions provide **Ongoing Assessment: Observing Students at Work** opportunities:

- **Session 1.1, p. 28**
- **Session 1.2, pp. 35–36**
- **Session 1.3, p. 42**
- **Session 1.4, pp. 45–46**
- **Session 1.5, p. 50**
- **Session 2.1, pp. 65 and 67**
- **Session 2.2, pp. 72 and 73**
- **Session 2.3, p. 77**
- **Session 2.5, p. 86**
- **Session 3.1, p. 104**
- **Session 3.2, pp. 107 and 108**
- **Session 3.4, p. 117**

WRITING OPPORTUNITIES

The following sessions have **writing** opportunities for students to explain their mathematical thinking:

- **Session 1.1, pp. 26–29**
  Representing How Many We Are
- **Session 1.4, p. 44**
  Student Activity Book, p. 72
- **Sessions 3.1–3.3, pp. 100–113**
  Student Activity Book, p. 77
- **Sessions 3.4–3.5, pp. 116 and 120**
  How Many Are Here Today?

PORTFOLIO OPPORTUNITIES

The following sessions have work appropriate for a **portfolio:**

- **Session 1.1, p. 26**
  Representing How Many We Are
- **Sessions 1.2, 1.4–1.6, pp. 35, 47, 51, and 54**
  Counting Jar
- **Sessions 3.2–3.3, pp. 107 and 112**
  Student Activity Book, p. 77

Assessing the Benchmarks

Observing students as they engage in conversation about their ideas is a primary means to assess their mathematical understanding. Consider all of your students' work, not just the written assessments. See the chart below for suggestions about key activities to observe.

Assessment Checklists are introduced in Session 1.1, Session 1.4, and Session 2.2. Use these checklists to determine which students have met the benchmarks and which students have not. During Session 3.4 and Session 3.5 students complete an End-of-Unit Assessment in which they use attendance data to solve a problem and then show on paper how they solved the problem. Use the data you have collected about each student on the assessment charts to decide who you need to focus on as students complete the assessment.

Checklist Available

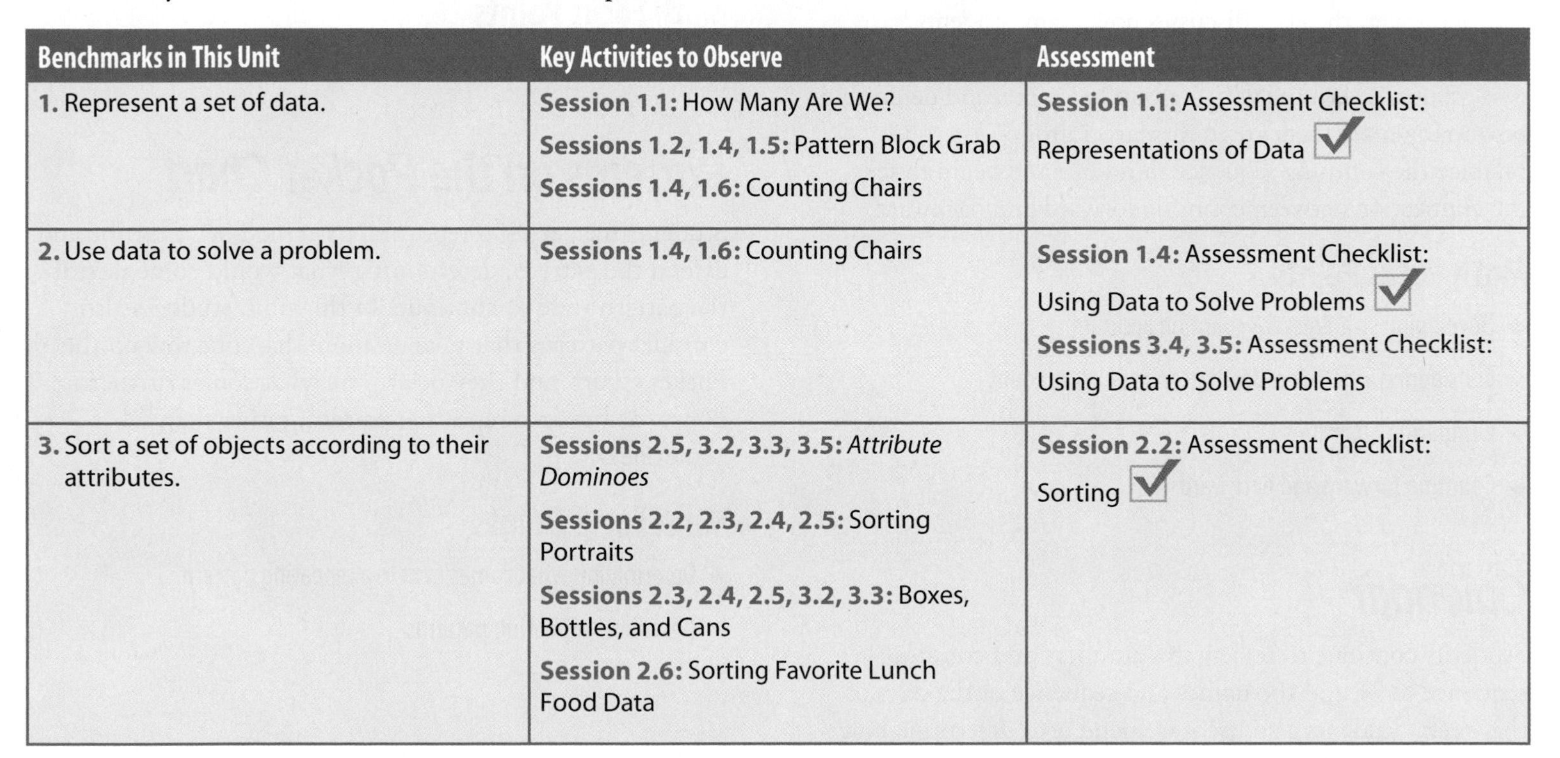

Benchmarks in This Unit	Key Activities to Observe	Assessment
1. Represent a set of data.	**Session 1.1:** How Many Are We? **Sessions 1.2, 1.4, 1.5:** Pattern Block Grab **Sessions 1.4, 1.6:** Counting Chairs	**Session 1.1:** Assessment Checklist: Representations of Data
2. Use data to solve a problem.	**Sessions 1.4, 1.6:** Counting Chairs	**Session 1.4:** Assessment Checklist: Using Data to Solve Problems **Sessions 3.4, 3.5:** Assessment Checklist: Using Data to Solve Problems
3. Sort a set of objects according to their attributes.	**Sessions 2.5, 3.2, 3.3, 3.5:** *Attribute Dominoes* **Sessions 2.2, 2.3, 2.4, 2.5:** Sorting Portraits **Sessions 2.3, 2.4, 2.5, 3.2, 3.3:** Boxes, Bottles, and Cans **Session 2.6:** Sorting Favorite Lunch Food Data	**Session 2.2:** Assessment Checklist: Sorting

Relating the Mathematical Emphases to the Benchmarks

Mathematical Emphases	Benchmarks
Counting and Quantity Developing strategies for accurately counting a set of objects by ones	
Data Analysis Representing data	1
Data Analysis Sorting and classifying	3
Data Analysis Carrying out a data investigation	2

Classroom Routines

IN THIS UNIT

Classroom Routines offer practice and review of key concepts for this grade level. These daily activities, to be done in 10 minutes outside of math class, occur in a regular rotation every 4–5 days. Specific directions for the day's routine are provided in each session. For the full description and variations of each classroom routine, see *Implementing Investigations in Kindergarten.*

Attendance

Students continue to count to determine the total number of students present and to explore what happens when the count begins with different students. In order to help students connect the counting numbers to the quantities they represent, the class discusses how many students have counted midway through the count. Students also compare two groups, determine which group has more, and determine how many more there are in this larger group. They also practice the counting sequence in reverse and begin to see the connection between counting forward and backward.

Math Focus Points

- Developing strategies for counting accurately
- Considering whether order matters when you count
- Comparing quantities
- Counting forward and backward

Calendar

Students continue to review the numbers and counting sequence to 31 and the names and sequence of the days of the week. Students also use the calendar to determine how many days until (or since) a special event and explain their strategies.

Math Focus Points

- Using the calendar as a tool for keeping track of time
- Developing strategies for counting accurately

Today's Question

Students record their response to a survey question with two possible answers on a two-column table. Class discussion focuses on describing and interpreting the data.

Math Focus Points

- Collecting, counting, representing, describing, and comparing data

Patterns on the Pocket Chart

Students see part of a repeating pattern. They describe and extend the pattern, determining what would come next if the pattern were to continue. In this unit, students also consider patterns that take up more than one row on the Pocket Chart, and they determine what comes further down the line in a repeating pattern, rather than what comes next.

Math Focus Points

- Determining what comes next in a repeating pattern
- Describing repeating patterns

Practice and Review

IN THIS UNIT

Practice and review play a critical role in the *Investigations* program. The following components and features are available to provide regular reinforcement of key mathematical concepts and procedures.

Books	Features	In This Unit . . .
Curriculum Unit	**Classroom Routines** offer practice and review of key concepts for this grade level. These daily activities, to be done in ten minutes outside of math class, occur in a regular rotation every 4–5 days. Specific directions for the day's routine are provided in each session. For the full description and variations of each classroom routine see *Implementing Investigations in Kindergarten.*	• **All sessions**
Student Activity Book	**Practice** pages in the *Student Activity Book* provide one of two types of written practice: **reinforcement** of the content of the unit or **enrichment** opportunities.	• **Session 1.5** • **Session 2.3** • **Session 2.6** • **Session 3.4**
	Homework pages in the *Student Activity Book* are an extension of the work done in class. At times they help students prepare for upcoming activities.	• **Session 1.3**
Student Math Handbook Flip Chart	**Math Words and Ideas** in the *Student Math Handbook Flip Chart* are pages that summarize key words and ideas. Most Words and Ideas pages have at least one exercise.	• **Student Math Handbook Flip Chart, pp. 18, 19, 20, 21, 22, 45, 46, 47, 48, 49**

Supporting the Range of Learners

Sessions	1.1	1.2	1.4	1.5	1.6	2.1	2.2	2.3	2.4	2.5	3.1	3.2	3.3	3.4
Intervention	•	•	•				•	•		•		•		•
Extension				•	•			•	•			•	•	
ELL			•			•				•	•		•	

Intervention

Suggestions are made to support and engage students who are having difficulty with a particular idea, activity, or problem.

Extension

Suggestions are made to support and engage students who finish early or may be ready for additional challenge.

English Language Learners (ELL)

In this unit, students develop ideas about counting and keeping track of quantities and working with one-to-one and two-to-one correspondence. They also learn to represent data, carry out a data investigation, sort and classify information, and use data to solve a problem. Because so many of the activities are language-based, English Language Learners may need one-on-one or small-group support in order to grasp the concepts that are presented throughout the unit.

After English Language Learners sort objects according to various attributes, they might need support explaining their rules. You can help by reviewing words that are commonly used to describe size, shape, and color. Work with a small group of English Language Learners to sort a collection of buttons according to different attributes.

Say: First, let's sort these buttons by *color.* Which color should we start with? OK, let's put all of the [*red*] buttons over here. Which color should we sort by next? Students can also sort the objects by size and shape. It might be helpful to create a chart listing relevant vocabulary to which English Language Learners can refer during other activities.

As students explore different types of data, they must also understand data-related terms such as *attribute, represent,* and *sort.* You can help by modeling this vocabulary in the context of activities such as *Pattern Block Grab.* Encourage English Language Learners to think aloud as they participate in various activities. Over time, they will become increasingly able to use this specialized vocabulary themselves.

Working with the Range of Learners: Classroom Cases is a set of episodes written by teachers that focuses on meeting the needs of the range of learners in the classroom. In the first section, *Setting up the Mathematical Community,* teachers write about how they create a supportive and productive learning environment in their classrooms. In the next section, *Accommodations for Learning,* teachers focus on specific modifications they make to meet the needs of some of their learners. In the last section, *Language and Representation,* teachers share how they help students use representations and develop language to investigate and express mathematical ideas. The questions at the end of each case provide a starting point for your own reflection or for discussion with colleagues. See *Implementing Investigations in Kindergarten* for this set of episodes.

INVESTIGATION 1

Mathematical Emphases

Counting and Quantity Developing strategies for accurately counting a set of objects by ones

Math Focus Points

- Counting and keeping track of quantities
- Matching sets with a one-to-one correspondence
- Working with two-to-one correspondence
- Counting by groups of 2

Data Analysis Representing data

Math Focus Points

- Making a representation of a set of data
- Seeing the one-to-one correspondence between a set of data and a representation of this data set

Data Analysis Carrying out a data investigation

Math Focus Points

- Using data to solve a problem

This Investigation also focuses on

- Comparing two quantities to determine which is more

How Many Noses? How Many Eyes?

	Student Activity Book	Student Math Handbook Flip Chart	Professional Development: Read Ahead of Time
SESSION 1.1 p. 24 **How Many Are We?** Students count the number of people in the class and then make representations that show the data they collected. Students share and compare their different representations.		18	• **Dialogue Box:** Why Do We Need to Know?, p. 138 • **Teacher Note:** Kindergarteners' Representations of Data, p. 123; One-to-One and Two-to-One Correspondence, p. 126 • **Mathematics in This Unit,** p. 10
SESSION 1.2 p. 31 **How Many Noses?** Students count the number of noses in the class. They learn a new game in which they grab a handful of pattern blocks and make a representation of the number and types of pattern blocks they grabbed. A new Counting Jar is introduced during Math Workshop.	70	19, 20	• **Teacher Note:** Dealing with Sensitive Issues, p. 128
SESSION 1.3 p. 37 **How Many Eyes?** Students count the number of eyes in the class and then make a class eye chart as a way to record the data. They look at the correspondence between the number of people and the number of eyes.	71		• **Dialogue Box:** How Many Eyes?, p. 139
SESSION 1.4 p. 43 **Counting Chairs** Students are introduced to Counting Chairs, an activity in which they count the number of chairs in the classroom and determine whether there are enough chairs for the students in the class. Math Workshop continues to focus on counting as a way of collecting data.	72	20, 21, 22	

Classroom Routines See page 16 for an overview.

Today's Question
- *Today's Question* charts for Sessions 1.2 and 1.6. See instructions on pages 31 and 53.

Calendar
- Class calendar

Patterns on the Pocket Chart
- Pocket chart(s) or sentence pocket chart
- M7, Question Mark Cards Cut apart.
- M6, Arrow Cards Cut apart.

Attendance
- No materials needed

Materials to Gather	Materials to Prepare
• **Materials for creating data representation such as connecting cubes, buttons, dot stickers, or 1-inch squares of colored paper** (as needed) • **Drawing supplies** (as needed) • **Glue sticks or tape** (as needed) • **12″ x 18″ paper** (1 sheet per student)	• **M3, Assessment Checklist: Representations of Data** ☑ Make copies. (3–4, plus extras if needed) • **M1–M2, Family Letter** Make copies. (1 per student) • **Collect containers** In Investigation 2, students will do a sorting activity using a variety of containers. Begin collecting 8–10 of each of the following containers: small boxes, empty plastic bottles, and unopened cans. You might want to ask students to contribute containers from home.
• **Connecting cubes** (bucket with at least 1 cube per student) • **Chart paper** • **Pattern blocks** (1 bucket per 3–4 students) • **Crayons or markers** (as needed) • **Materials for the Counting Jar routine** (as you have set it up)	• **Counting Jar** Place two of each type of pattern block in the jar. (12 blocks in all) • **M5, Pattern Block Grab** Make copies. (as needed)
• **Index cards or slips of paper, 3″ x 5″** (3–10 per student) • **Crayons or markers** (as needed) • **Tape or glue sticks** (as needed) • **Mirrors** (optional; as needed) • **Envelopes** (1 per student)	• **Chart paper** Prepare a chart titled "Body Parts That Come in Twos." • **Chart paper** Prepare an eye data chart approximately 8 inches wide by about 6 feet long (long enough to hold an index card for each student in the class). • **Chart paper** Prepare a 2-column chart titled "People and Eyes." Title one column "People" and the other "Eyes." See page 41.
• **Counters such as connecting cubes, buttons, or chips** (about 50 of each) • **Chart paper** (optional) • **Crayons or markers** • **Materials for Pattern Block Grab** See Session 1.2. • **Materials for Counting Jar** See Session 1.2.	• **M4, Assessment Checklist: Using Data to Solve Problems** ☑ Make copies. (3–4 per class, plus extras as needed)

☑ Checklist Available

How Many Noses? How Many Eyes?, *continued*

	Student Activity Book	Student Math Handbook Flip Chart	Professional Development: Read Ahead of Time	
SESSION 1.5 p. 48				
Eyes at Home Students are introduced to Eyes at Home in which they count the number of eyes in the homes of students in the class. Math Workshop continues to focus on counting as a way of collecting data. The session ends with a discussion about representing handfuls of pattern blocks.	70, 73–74			
SESSION 1.6 p. 53				
Enough Chairs for the Class? Math Workshop continues to focus on counting and collecting data. The session ends with a discussion about how students counted the chairs in the class and how they determined whether there are enough chairs for everyone.		19, 20, 21, 22		

	Materials to Gather	Materials to Prepare
	• **Students' completed Eyes at Home data** (1 envelope per student) • **Materials for Counting Chairs** See Session 1.4. • **Materials for Pattern Block Grab** See Session 1.2. • **Materials for Counting Jar** See Session 1.2. • **Pattern blocks** (1 bin)	• **Eyes at Home Sample Envelope** Prepare a sample Eyes at Home to show students. Draw a pair of eyes on an index card for each person who lives in your home. Put the index cards in an envelope and write your name on it.
	• **Materials for Eyes at Home** See Session 1.5. • **Materials for Counting Chairs** See Session 1.4. • **Materials for Counting Jar** See Session 1.2.	

How Many Are We?

Math Focus Points

- Counting and keeping track of quantities
- Making a representation of a set of data
- Seeing the one-to-one correspondence between a set of data and a representation of this data set

Today's Plan		Materials
1 ACTIVITY **How Many Are We?**	5–10 MIN CLASS	
2 ACTIVITY **Representing How Many We Are**	15–25 MIN INDIVIDUALS	• M3* ☑ • Connecting cubes, buttons, dot stickers, 1-inch squares of colored paper; drawing supplies; glue sticks or tape; 12″ x 18″ paper
3 DISCUSSION **Sharing Representations**	10 MIN CLASS	
4 SESSION FOLLOW-UP **Homework**		• *Student Math Handbook Flip Chart,* p. 18 • M1–M2, Family Letter*

*See *Materials to Prepare,* p. 21.

Classroom Routines

Attendance: How Many Have Counted? Count around the circle as usual, but pause several times during the count to ask students how many people have counted so far and how they know. Help students see why the numbers they say represent the numbers of students who have counted so far and that the last number represents the total number of students in class today.

ACTIVITY 1

How Many Are We?

This activity builds on *Attendance*, the familiar Classroom Routine, which has been used throughout the year.

In the next few weeks, we will be collecting a lot of information about ourselves. We can find out some important information by counting. We've counted the number of people in our class a lot of times this year, and today we will do it again. Can you think of any reasons why you or I or other people might need to know how many of us there are? ①

Collect ideas from the students, encouraging them to explain their thinking.

First, let's take attendance like we've done before.

Next, ask for ideas about how to count the people in the class, making sure everyone is counted, even absent students. The size of the class will already be quite familiar to your students. Even so, discussing ways to determine the size of a group is good preparation for making representations of that group.

Students are likely to have many ideas, including counting names on a class list, counting students' cubbies, and counting around the circle and then adding in any absent students.

How can we make sure that we don't count anyone twice? Who has a way that would help us keep track of which people we have counted and which people we have not counted? What about people who are absent today?

Students might say:

"We can count the kids as they stand up and then count the people who are not here."

"Everyone can take one cube. We can put all the cubes together and count them. We'll have to put in more cubes for the kids who are sick."

Professional Development

① **Dialogue Box:** Why Do We Need to Know?, p. 138

Teaching Notes

❷ **Assembling a Portfolio** Representing the number of students in the class is students' first opportunity to represent a data set. Include these representations in portfolios as records of how students first represented data.

❸ **Assessing Students' Representation of Data** By the end of this unit, students are expected to be able to represent a set of data (Benchmark 1). This means that they represent the number of pieces of data accurately, organize the data, and represent the data so that other people can gather information from the representation. Use Assessment Checklist: Representations of Data (M3) to keep track of your observations about students' representations of data over the course of this investigation and unit.

Professional Development

❹ **Teacher Note:** Kindergarteners' Representations of Data, p. 123

"Each person can make a mark on the board. We can put in marks for the people who are missing."

Suppose we counted the people in our class in two different ways. Should we get the same number of people? Why or why not?

Some students will know there should be the same number of students no matter how they are counted. Other students may not be so sure.

Students count the number of people in the class.

Try a few of the counting strategies that students suggest. When all students agree on a total, post the information. For example, "There are 25 people in our class."

ACTIVITY

Representing How Many We Are

15–25 MIN INDIVIDUALS

Explain to students that they are now going to figure out a way to show the total number of students in the class when everyone is present.❷

Each of you will find one way to show this information. We have lots of different materials you can use. Here is what's most important: When you have finished, someone who knows nothing about our class should be able to look at what you made and tell how many of us there are.❸ ❹

Students make representations of the number of people in the class.

Point out the available materials—various counters and drawing supplies—and ask for students' ideas about how they could use the materials to show how many students are in the class. The more materials you offer, the greater variety of representations students are likely to generate.

Some students may start by building physical models to represent the number of children in the classroom. Encourage these children to also draw a picture (even a picture of their physical model) to keep a record of their work. For example, if a student builds a tower of 25 cubes, ask how he or she could show this on paper with a picture. A student who has collected 25 beans or other items might glue them onto a sheet of paper for a permanent record.

Be aware that some students may just want to write a number to indicate the number of students in the class. When this is the case, encourage them to make a picture or find a way to show "how many" that number represents.

When you make your drawing or representation of how many people are in our class, also write down the number so others can easily tell how many there are.

As students finish their work, suggest that they write or dictate a title for their picture.❺ ❻ ❼

Professional Development

❺ **Teacher Note:** One-to-One and Two-to-One Correspondence, p. 126

Math Notes

❻ **25 Buttons for 25 Students** While many students will realize that the quantities of items in their representations should equal the number of students in the class, this will not be obvious to some students who are still working on the idea of the relationship between the counting sequence and quantities.

❼ **Counting Above 20** Counting a set of up to 20 objects is a benchmark in *How Many Do You Have?* In this unit, students are working with data from their class, so they may be counting and representing quantities above 20. Because they have worked with this number consistently throughout the Classroom Routines of *Attendance* and *Today's Question*, students are likely to be very familiar with this number and combinations of this number.

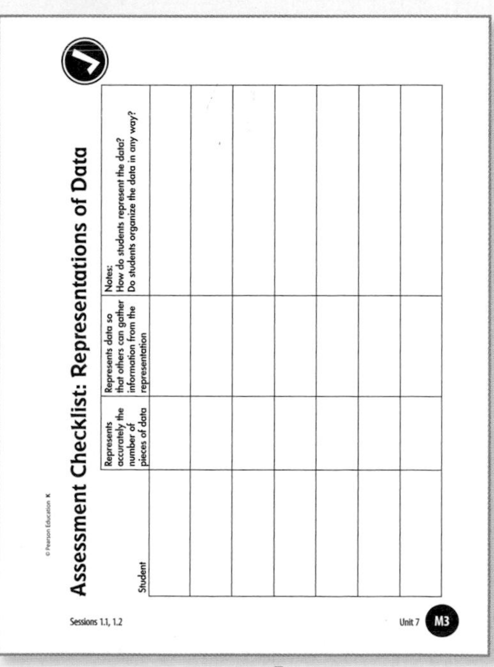

Assessment Checklist: Representations of Data

Student	Represents accurately the number of pieces of data	Represents data so that others can gather information from the representation	Notes: How do students represent the data? Do students organize the data in any way?

Sessions 1.1, 1.2 Unit 7 M3

▲ Resource Masters, M3

ONGOING ASSESSMENT: Observing Students at Work

Students make a representation that shows the total number of students in the class.

- **How do students represent the number of students in the class?** Do the representations in fact account for everyone in the class?
- **How do students keep track of the items in their representations?**
- **How do students count the items in their representations?** Do they compare this count to the known information about the number of people in the class?

As students are working, ask individual students about their work.

Assessment Checklist: Representations of Data

Student	Represents accurately the number of pieces of data	Represents data so that others can gather information from the representation	Notes: How do students represent the data? Do students organize the data in any way?
Kyle How many are we?	✓	✓ numbered people	drew 22 people & numbered them people all over page
Rebecca How many are we?	no, 20 not 22	✓ wrong "students in my class"	made 20 circles in one row and difficulty counting above 20?
Sharonne How many are we?	✓	✓	made 2 towers of cubes one of 10 green - labeled girls one of 12 blue - labeled boys
Dennis How many are we?	✓ but doesn't know how many lines when I asked	no, lines all over page	drew 22 lines scattered not numbered. watch him again.

How do you know your picture shows exactly the number of students in the class? What does each dot (or mark or stick figure) stand for? How does the number you have written go with the picture you have made?

DIFFERENTIATION: Supporting the Range of Learners

Intervention If your class is larger than 20, some students might have difficulty counting and representing this quantity. It may help some students to build a physical model of the data using cubes and a class list so that they can match one item to each student. Students can then touch and move each item as they count them.

Intervention If you know some students will have trouble counting over 20, ask the students to divide their papers and show the number of boys on one side and the number of girls on the other side. By breaking the group into two, these students may be more successful in counting the total number of students.

DISCUSSION

Sharing Representations

10 MIN CLASS

Math Focus Points for Discussion

- Making a representation of a set of data

Gather students to discuss and share their representations. If students are bringing their work to a rug area, suggest that they sit in a circle and place their work in the center or display their work on the wall or board.

You've found many different ways to show information about how many people we are. What's the same about these pictures? What's different?

Students are likely to notice things like the types of materials people used or the ways that some people used dots. Some might have made drawings of people, and others might have used cubes to show each piece of data.

Ask a few students who have represented the data in different ways to explain their work to the group.

Knowing exactly how many of us there are will be helpful during the next few weeks as we collect different kinds of information about the people in our class.

Display as many of the students' representations as possible, or bind them into a book for future reference.

SESSION FOLLOW-UP

4 Homework

Student Math Handbook Flip Chart: Use the *Student Math Handbook Flip Chart* page 18 to reinforce concepts from today's session.

Family Letter: Send home copies of the Family Letter (M1–M2) with each student.

How Many Noses?

Math Focus Points

- Matching sets with a one-to-one correspondence
- Counting and keeping track of quantities
- Making a representation of a set of data

Today's Plan	Time	Grouping	Materials
DISCUSSION **1 How Many Noses?**	5–10 MIN	CLASS	• Connecting cubes; chart paper
ACTIVITY **2 Introducing Pattern Block Grab**	5 MIN	CLASS	• M5* • Pattern blocks
MATH WORKSHOP **3 Counting and Representing** 3A Pattern Block Grab 3B Counting Jar	15–25 MIN		3A • *Student Activity Book*, p. 70 • Pattern blocks; crayons or markers • M3 ✓ 3B • Counting Jar*; materials for doing the Counting Jar (as you have set it up)
DISCUSSION **4 Checking In**	5 MIN	CLASS	
SESSION FOLLOW-UP **5 Practice**			• *Student Math Handbook Flip Chart*, pp. 19, 20

* See *Materials to Prepare*, p. 21.

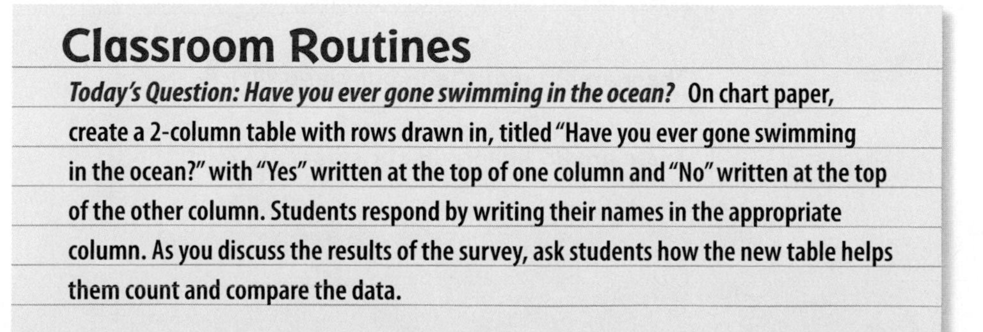

Classroom Routines

Today's Question: Have you ever gone swimming in the ocean? On chart paper, create a 2-column table with rows drawn in, titled "Have you ever gone swimming in the ocean?" with "Yes" written at the top of one column and "No" written at the top of the other column. Students respond by writing their names in the appropriate column. As you discuss the results of the survey, ask students how the new table helps them count and compare the data.

Teaching Note

❶ **Number of Noses Equals Number of Students** By this time of the year, many students will be convinced that there are the same number of noses as there are people in the class. A few may not connect their previous experiences with class attendance with this new way of looking at the question.

DISCUSSION

1 How Many Noses?

5–10 MIN CLASS

Math Focus Points for Discussion

- Matching sets with a one-to-one correspondence

Yesterday we counted the number of students in our class and then found a way to show how many people are in our class. Suppose we wanted to know how many noses there are in our class. How many noses do you think there would be if everyone was here?❶

As students offer their ideas about how many noses there are, encourage them to explain their reasoning.

Tell students that you will be making a "tower of noses." Each student will take a connecting cube to represent his or her nose. Pass around a bucket of cubes so each student can take one. Then ask students to make a class tower by snapping their cubes together. As students add their cubes to the class tower, they count off as they have done in the past. Include absent students in the count by adding cubes at the end.

When they have finished, ask students how many cubes are in the tower of noses. When students agree on this number, write it on the board or a sheet of chart paper.

If we know that there are [25] noses in our class, *what else* do we know there are [25] of?

Add students' ideas to make a data chart. Add a sketch to help students identify any new words.

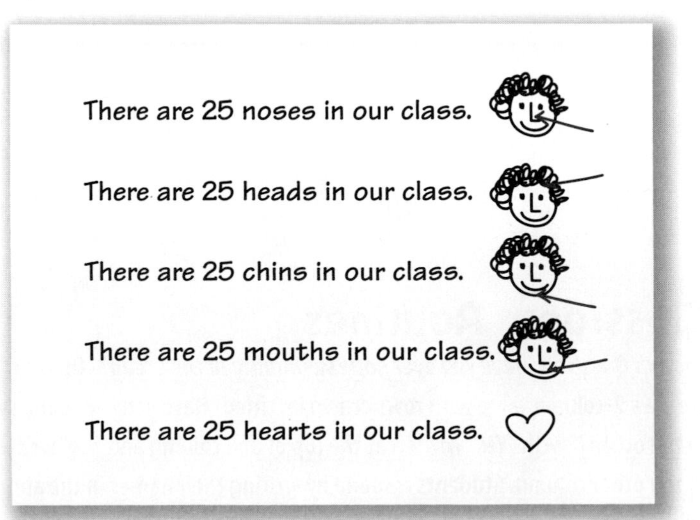

During this discussion, if anyone suggests things that people have *more* than one of, such as ears, legs, teeth, hair, fingers, or eyes, begin a second list of these on a separate sheet of chart paper. You can use this list during the next session to initiate the activity about how many eyes. Note that this activity might evoke sensitive issues in some classrooms.❷

More than 1

ears

eyes

hands

hair

teeth

ACTIVITY

2 Introducing Pattern Block Grab

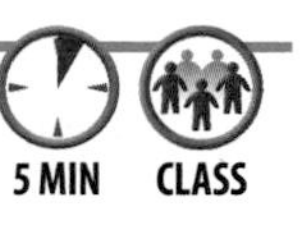

Explain to students that you are going to introduce them to an activity that they will be doing during Math Workshop. This activity is a variation of *Grab and Count* in which students grab a handful of objects and count them. However, in this variation, they are also counting how many there are of each kind of block.

How many pattern blocks do you think I can grab with one hand?

Solicit a few responses from students and then take a handful of blocks. Lay them out and ask different students to count each type of block.❸

We found out that I grabbed [three hexagons, two triangles, two squares, six tan rhombuses, three blue rhombuses, and one trapezoid]. How can I figure out how many blocks I grabbed altogether?

Many students will suggest counting all the blocks, but some students may suggest other strategies such as using combinations that they know or counting on. Try a few of their suggested methods, then direct students' attention to *Student Activity Book* page 70 or Pattern Block Grab (M5).

Professional Development

❷ **Teacher Note:** Dealing with Sensitive Issues, p. 128

Teaching Note

❸ **What's a Handful?** As a class, discuss and agree upon what constitutes a "handful." Some groups of students have used the rule that after you grab a handful, you shake off any loose blocks and that's your handful.

Name Date

Sorting and Surveys

Pattern Block Grab

Grab a handful of pattern blocks.
Show how many of each.

How many did you grab in all? ______

Grab a handful of pattern blocks.
Show how many of each.

How many did you grab in all? ______

70 Unit 7 Session 1.2

© Pearson Education K

▲ **Student Activity Book, p. 70; Resource Masters, M5**

Teaching Note

④ **Assessing Students' Representations of Data** Observing students' representations of the data from their Pattern Block Grab presents another opportunity to assess students' representations of data. Use Assessment Checklist: Representations of Data (M3) to keep track of your observations about students' data representations over the course of this investigation and unit.

How could I show on this page how many of each kind I grabbed?

Ask two or three students to share their ideas for recording. Explain to students that they will be collecting information about how many patterns blocks they can grab and showing that information on their student sheet. Emphasize that they need to show not only how many blocks they grabbed in all but also how many of each type of block they grabbed.

What if I just drew one of each type of block I grabbed—what if I drew a blue rhombus, a hexagon, and a triangle because these are the kinds of blocks I grabbed. Would that show you how many of each type of block I grabbed? . . . How could I change my drawing so that it showed how many of each type of block I grabbed?

MATH WORKSHOP

3 Counting and Representing

15–25 MIN

Show students the new Counting Jar.

Explain that the following two activities are available during this Math Workshop. Remind students what materials are required and where they are located.

3A Pattern Block Grab

INDIVIDUALS

Students grab a handful of pattern blocks and then make a representation of the types and numbers of pattern blocks they grabbed. They record how many blocks they grabbed in all on *Student Activity Book* page 70.④

Students grab a handful of pattern blocks and count how many of each type and how many total they grabbed.

ONGOING ASSESSMENT: Observing Students at Work

Students count subsets of objects, represent the data on paper, and then determine how many in all.

- **Do students organize their blocks according to the type of block?**
- **Do students accurately count and record each type of block, as well as the total?**
- **How do students represent their handful of blocks?** Do they show each block? Do they use symbols such as "S" for square, and "H" for hexagon and then write the number? Do they draw one block and then the number of how many?

DIFFERENTIATION: Supporting the Range of Learners

Intervention Some students may have difficulty figuring out how to count and record the number of each type of block they grabbed. For these students, suggest the following: organize the blocks according to type, draw a sketch of each block, and then write the number of blocks in that group. For students who struggle with drawing each block, have them record using paper pattern blocks. Resource Masters for these can be found in *What Comes Next?* or the *Make a Shape, Build a Block*.

3B Counting Jar

INDIVIDUALS

Students count a set of pattern blocks (two of each type, 12 blocks in all) in the Counting Jar. They make a set of the same size, and then find a way to record what they found out.[5]

ONGOING ASSESSMENT: Observing Students at Work

Students count a set of objects, create an equivalent set, and record their work.

- **How do students count the objects in the jar?** Do they organize the objects in any way? Do they count each item once and only once? Do they double-check?
- **Do they use the pairs of pattern blocks to figure out the total?** Do they count by twos? Group the pairs into larger groups?

Teaching Note

5 Assembling a Portfolio Because students do Counting Jar in every unit, this activity provides an opportunity to see students' growth over time. For one of the Counting Jars in this unit, have students record their work on a piece of paper you can collect and put in their portfolios.

- **How do students create an equivalent set?** Do they think, "The Counting Jar had 12. I need 12 tiles. 1, 2, 3 . . ."? Do they recreate the Counting Jar set, matching them 1 to 1? Do they double-check?
- **How do students record their work?**

4 DISCUSSION
Checking In

Briefly check in with students about their work on Pattern Block Grab. Check in with them about any issues that came up as they grabbed a handful. Consider asking one or two students to show how they recorded the data for this activity.

5 SESSION FOLLOW-UP
Practice

Student Math Handbook Flip Chart: Use the *Student Math Handbook Flip Chart* pages 19, 20 to reinforce content from today's session. See pages 146–148 in the back of this unit.

SESSION 1.3

How Many Eyes?

Math Focus Points

- Working with two-to-one correspondence
- Counting by groups of 2
- Counting and keeping track of quantities
- Making a representation of a set of data

Vocabulary

count

Today's Plan		Materials
1 ACTIVITY **Introducing How Many Eyes?**	10–15 MIN CLASS	• Chart: "Body Parts that Come in Twos"*
2 ACTIVITY **How Many Eyes?**	20–30 MIN INDIVIDUALS CLASS	• Index cards or slips of paper, 3″ x 5″; crayons or markers; tape or glue sticks; mirrors; chart: eye data*; chart: "People and Eyes"*
3 SESSION FOLLOW-UP **Homework**		• *Student Activity Book,* p. 71 • Index cards or slips of paper, 3″ x 5″; envelopes

*See *Materials to Prepare,* p. 21.

Classroom Routines

Calendar: How Many Days . . . ? **Students use the calendar to determine how many days have passed since a class event or holiday that happened this month, or for a challenge, an event that occurred last month. Discuss students' strategies for determining the number of days.**

Math Note

❶ **Two-to-one correspondence** Some students may relate the number of eyes to the previous activity of counting noses. Listen for phrases such as *twice as many, double the number, and two for each.* These are important indicators that students are beginning to develop an understanding of two-to-one correspondence, even though few kindergarteners will be able to double the number of noses in the classroom. Some students might suggest counting by 2s as a strategy for counting the number of eyes. Some students may be able to chant 2, 4, 6, 8 but not be able to continue the sequence or know how the sequence fits this situation. Others may be able to apply this counting strategy with meaning and understanding.

Professional Development

❷ **Teacher Note:** One-to-One and Two-to-One Correspondence, p. 126

❸ **Dialogue Box:** How Many Eyes?, p. 139

Teaching Note

❹ **Counting Students Who Are Absent** In one class, the teacher drew two eyes on different index cards to represent the absent students. In another class, the students had stuffed animals to stand in for the absent students.

ACTIVITY 1

Introducing How Many Eyes?

10–15 MIN CLASS

Post the chart you prepared titled "Body Parts That Come in Twos," and direct students' attention to it.

We all have one nose, but there are some things on our body that come in twos. Who can think of some of those?

Ask students to name or point out body parts that come in pairs. List them on the chart. Be sure that eyes are listed.

Suppose we wanted to count how many eyes there are in our class when everyone is here. How could we do that so we would have the exact number of eyes?

Ask students to turn to their partners and briefly talk about how they would count the number of eyes. Then ask a few students to share their strategies for counting. Encourage them to explain how they would keep track of the number of eyes.❶ ❷ ❸

Choose one of the suggested methods to count the eyes in your class.❹

It is a good idea to link the counting of each eye with some physical movement to help students associate the numbers with the objects being counted. It is also helpful to double-check the count using a different strategy. When the count is complete, write this information on chart paper or on the board. As with the "nose" list, extend this "eye" list with other body parts that come in twos.

If we each have two eyes and there are [50] eyes in our classroom, how many legs do you think there are in our classroom? How could we check that information?

Take a count of legs, and add this information to the data chart. Include a picture to represent each part counted.❺

After counting the number of eyes in the class, students count other body parts that come in twos.

ACTIVITY 2

How Many Eyes?

Explain that the class is now going to work to represent the eye data by making a picture that shows the information about how many eyes there are in the class.

Distribute the index cards or slips of paper and drawing materials for each student to make a picture of his or her own eyes. If you have mirrors available, students can research the shape of their eyes, the color, and the parts (e.g., pupil, lid, lashes). Students should work on their eye cards for about 10 minutes.

Gather students together again to collect the eye data. Post the eye data chart oriented vertically. As students finish their eye cards, glue or tape them onto this strip, starting at the bottom, to make a tall tower of eye cards. Note that this is not to be a graph of categories, such as eye colors, but rather a simple representation of all the eyes in the classroom. When all the cards have been added, ask students to suggest a name for the chart and write it at the top of the paper. Then discuss ways to count all of the eyes shown.

Teaching Note

❺ **Counting Body Parts** Counting other body parts can be an ongoing activity during future whole class meetings. If your students generate a lot of strategies for counting, list their ideas on chart paper so they can choose different strategies for future counts. Kindergarteners typically like strategies that involve physical movement, such as raising both hands and putting them down as they are counted or stamping each foot as it is counted.

Suppose we were going to count the number of eyes on our eye chart. How many eyes do you think there are?

Some students are likely to connect this information to the eye count that they just completed, although not all kindergarteners will make this association. Ask the class to count with you as you point to each eye on the chart. Many students may not be able to count this high on their own; by counting together, everyone gets experience with counting to a relatively high number. Verify the result of the count with the information you wrote on chart paper or the board earlier.

Suppose one of your parents or another teacher from our school came into our classroom and looked at our eye chart. What kind of information could he or she get from it? Could someone tell how many eyes there are in our class just by looking at the chart? How could he or she figure out this information?

Many students will realize that the number of eyes on the chart represents the number of eyes in the class. However, some students may not yet connect this representation on paper to the number of eyes in the classroom.

If no one mentions the number of people in the class, ask:

Could they tell how many people are in our class just by looking at the chart? How could they figure that out?

Some kindergarteners will make the connection between the number of students in class and the number of cards on the chart. The fact that the cards represent both the number of people in the class and each pair of eyes may be a difficult idea for many students to grasp.

To help students with this idea and as another way of representing the data, ask the students to help you put the eye data into the chart you prepared titled "People and Eyes."

Where it says "People," we are going to make a list of how many people we have counted altogether. Where it says "Eyes," we are going to make a list of how many eyes that number of people have.

Starting at the bottom of the eye tower, ask whose eyes they are. That student should say the number "one," counting off as you do in the attendance routine. Write the number 1 in the people column and the number 2 in the eye column.

So far, we have counted one person and two eyes altogether.

Ask the next person to count off as you write the number 2 in the people column.

Now we have counted two people. How many eyes do we have altogether if we have two people?

Take suggestions for how many eyes two people have, and ask students to explain their thinking.

Continue with the third and fourth person, asking children how many eyes they have altogether after each of these additions. After the fourth person, ask the class to count with you as you add more people to the list. Once you have completed the list, verify the result of the count with the information you wrote on the chart paper earlier.

People and Eyes

People	Eyes
1	2
2	4
3	6
4	8
5	

When the list is finished, ask students to look at it carefully.

What do you notice about the numbers on the eye chart? Is there a pattern that you see?

Students might say:

"The numbers go up fast for eyes. The number for people goes slow."

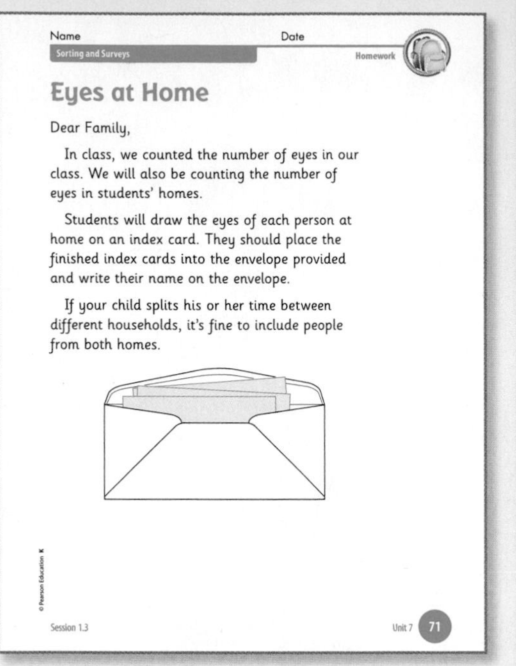

Name Date

Sorting and Surveys Homework

Eyes at Home

Dear Family,

In class, we counted the number of eyes in our class. We will also be counting the number of eyes in students' homes.

Students will draw the eyes of each person at home on an index card. They should place the finished index cards into the envelope provided and write their name on the envelope.

If your child splits his or her time between different households, it's fine to include people from both homes.

Session 1.3 Unit 7 71

▲ Student Activity Book, p. 71

"There are more eyes than kids."

"The eyes go like this: 2, 4, 6, 8."

A goal is for children to begin to see that each card represents one person and more than one eye. This is a step toward multiplicative thinking that not all children of this age are ready to take. Repeated experiences with counting by 1s *and* counting by groups will enable students to establish a foundation for repeated addition and multiplication.

ONGOING ASSESSMENT: Observing Students at Work

Students collect data on the number of eyes in the class by making a representation and counting the number of eyes.

- **Do students recognize that there must be more eyes all together than there are people all together?**
- **Do students understand that each card simultaneously represents one person and two eyes?**
- **Do students notice a relationship or pattern between the number of people and number of eyes?**
- **Can students accurately count the number of eyes?**

3 SESSION FOLLOW-UP

Homework

Homework: Students draw the eyes of each person in their home on an index card. They put their index cards with eyes on them in an envelope and write their name on the envelope. They will need to bring in their completed homework by Session 1.5 when they will begin to use them for the Eyes at Home activity. Send each student home with 2–10 3″ x 5″ index cards, an envelope, and *Student Activity Book* page 71, which explains the homework assignment.

Counting Chairs

Math Focus Points

- Counting and keeping track of quantities
- Using data to solve a problem
- Comparing two quantities to determine which is more

Today's Plan		Materials
1 ACTIVITY **Introducing Counting Chairs**	5–10 MIN CLASS	• *Student Activity Book,* p. 72 • Counters such as connecting cubes, buttons, chips; chart paper
2 MATH WORKSHOP **Counting Chairs and Pattern Blocks** 2A Counting Chairs 2B Pattern Block Grab 2C Counting Jar	15–25 MIN	2A • *Student Activity Book,* p. 72 • M4 ☑ * • Counters such as connecting cubes, buttons, chips; crayons or markers 2B • Materials from Session 1.2, p. 31 2C • Materials from Session 1.2, p. 31
3 DISCUSSION **Checking In**	5 MIN CLASS	
4 SESSION FOLLOW-UP **Practice**		• *Student Math Handbook Flip Chart,* pp. 20, 21, 22

*See *Materials to Prepare,* p. 21.

Classroom Routines

Patterns on the Pocket Chart: What Comes Here? Arrange an ABC repeating pattern on the first two rows of the pocket chart using 14 or more Arrow Cards (M6) (e.g., left, up, right). Cover the 8th through the last Arrow Card with Question Mark Cards (M7). Follow the basic *Patterns* activity but instead of asking for the *next* direction in the pattern sequence, point to the 12th pocket and ask students what direction is under the Question Mark Card. Students point in the direction they think it is.

Teaching Note

❶ **Do We Count *All* of the Chairs?** Discuss and decide as a class whether just the student chairs or *all* of the chairs (e.g., student chairs, teacher chairs, computer chairs) in the class will be counted. Also clarify that the number of "everyone in the class" is the number the class determined in Session 1.1 in the How Many Are We? activity.

Name Date

Sorting and Surveys

Counting Chairs

1. You can keep track of the number of chairs you count here.

2. How many chairs are in our class? ______

3. Are there enough chairs for everyone in the class? ______

72 Unit 7 Session 1.4

▲ **Student Activity Book, p. 72**

ACTIVITY 1

Introducing Counting Chairs

To introduce the activity, ask students how many chairs they think you have in the classroom. Record their guesses on the board or on chart paper.

Suppose we wanted to find out exactly how many chairs there are in our room. How could we do that?

After a few students have shared their ideas, explain that they will be counting the chairs in the room as a Math Workshop activity. They will decide on a way to count, take the count, and then record the number of chairs on *Student Activity Book* page 72.❶

Show students numbers 1 and 2 on the Activity page. Explain that they can use the space under number 1 to keep track of their count, but that they can also use other methods to keep track of their count.

Think about how you'll keep track of your count. You might make marks or put dots on *Student Activity Book* page 72, or you might use counters such as cubes or buttons. When you've finished counting, record how many chairs there are on the page 72.

Then explain the problem students solve using the data of the number of chairs in the class. Show them number 3 on *Student Activity Book* page 72.

Do you think there are enough chairs for everyone in this class to have one? Why do you think so? . . . This is a problem you are going to solve. After you have written down the number of chairs in the classroom on *Student Activity Book* page 72, you are going to figure out if there are enough chairs for every person in our class. Are there any extra chairs? Do we need more chairs?

Show them where on *Student Activity Book* page 72 they can record whether there are enough chairs for everyone.

MATH WORKSHOP

2 Counting Chairs and Pattern Blocks

15–25 MIN

Explain that the following three activities are available during this Math Workshop. Remind students what materials are required and where they are located.

2A Counting Chairs

Students count the number of chairs in the classroom and can use a variety of materials to keep track of their count. They then determine whether they have enough chairs for all the students in the class and record how they know whether there are enough chairs for everyone in the class.❷

Students count the number of chairs in the classroom and use a variety of materials to keep track of and record their counts.

ONGOING ASSESSMENT: Observing Students at Work

Students count a number of large objects and determine whether that number is smaller than or greater than the number of students in the class.

- **Do students have a system for counting the number of chairs and keeping track of which they have counted and which they have not?**
- **Do students count and record the number of chairs accurately?** How do they represent the data of how many chairs there are?
- **Can students determine whether there are enough chairs for everyone in the class?**

Teaching Note

❷ **Assessing Students as They Use Data to Solve Problems** By the end of this unit, students are expected to be able to use data to solve a problem (Benchmark 2). This means that they identify data to use to solve a problem, accurately solve the problem, and explain or show how they solved the problem. Use Assessment Checklist: Using Data to Solve Problems (M4) to keep track of your observations about students using data to solve problems over the course of this Investigation and unit.

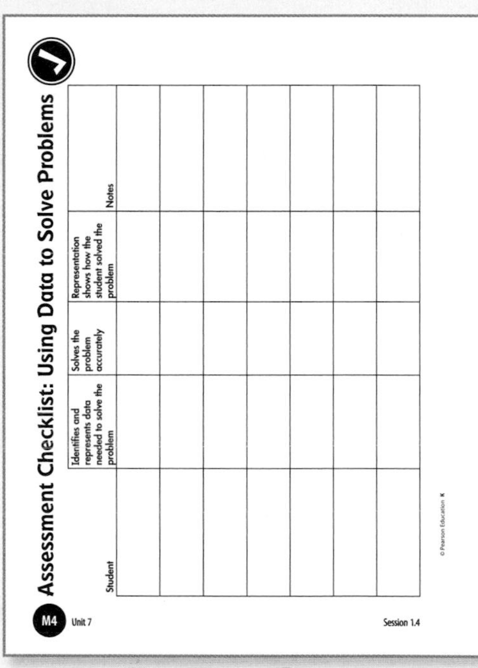

Assessment Checklist: Using Data to Solve Problems

Student	Identifies and represents data needed to solve the problem	Solves the problem accurately	Representation shows how the student solved the problem	Notes

M4 Unit 7 Session 1.4

© Pearson Education K

▲ Resource Masters, M4

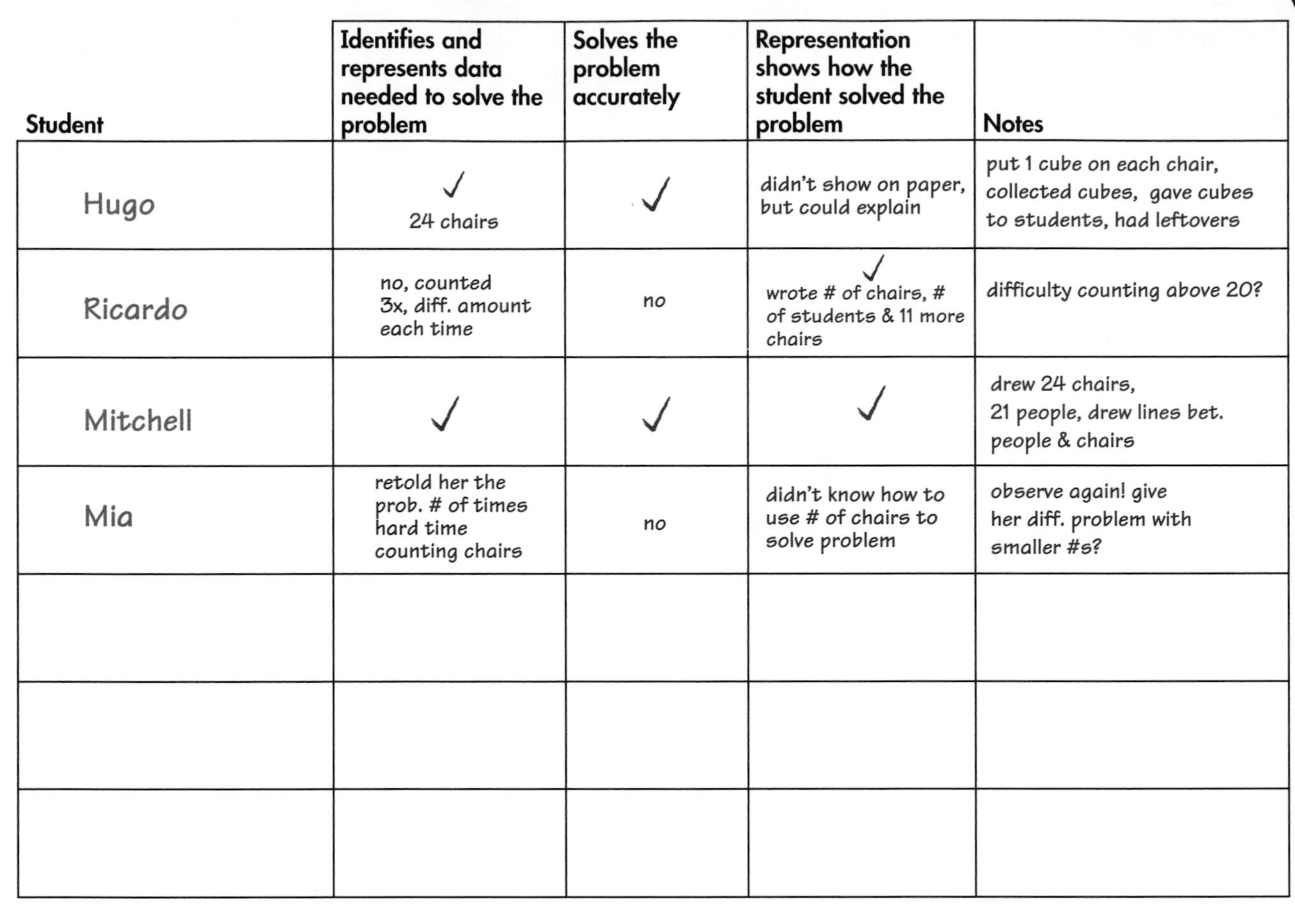

Assessment Checklist: Using Data to Solve Problems

Student	Identifies and represents data needed to solve the problem	Solves the problem accurately	Representation shows how the student solved the problem	Notes
Hugo	✓ 24 chairs	✓	didn't show on paper, but could explain	put 1 cube on each chair, collected cubes, gave cubes to students, had leftovers
Ricardo	no, counted 3x, diff. amount each time	no	✓ wrote # of chairs, # of students & 11 more chairs	difficulty counting above 20?
Mitchell	✓	✓	✓	drew 24 chairs, 21 people, drew lines bet. people & chairs
Mia	retold her the prob. # of times hard time counting chairs	no	didn't know how to use # of chairs to solve problem	observe again! give her diff. problem with smaller #s?

DIFFERENTIATION: Supporting the Range of Learners

Intervention For students for whom counting above 15 or 20 is difficult, counting and recording the number of chairs will be challenging enough. They do not have to solve the problem about whether there are enough chairs for everyone in the class.

ELL Some English Language Learners may need help understanding the word *enough*. You can gather students in a small group to demonstrate the meaning of the word in context.

I brought some pencils for you to use in class today, but I'm not sure whether I have enough of them. Let's see if I have enough. [Hand a pencil to all but one or two students.] Does everyone have a pencil?

(*No.*) Uh-oh, we don't have enough pencils. I'd better get some more. [Hand pencils to the remaining students.] Does everyone have a pencil now? (*Yes.*) Good, now we have enough.

Have English Language Learners repeat the exercise using other objects.

2B Pattern Block Grab

For complete details about this activity, see Session 1.2, page 33.

2C Counting Jar

INDIVIDUALS

For complete details about this activity, see Session 1.2, page 35.

DISCUSSION

Checking In

Take this opportunity to discuss any issues that you noticed while observing students at work. The topic might be mathematical in nature, such as some strategies you would like all students to consider (e.g., ways to keep track of the number of chairs students have counted and which ones they have left to count) or a common error or misconception you would like students to discuss (e.g., students writing the numbers above 20 incorrectly).

It could also be a logistical issue, such as clarifying the steps of the Counting Chairs activity, or a management issue, for example, not disturbing others as they work on the Counting Chairs activity.

Other alternatives include checking in with students about which activities they have been choosing (e.g., "Who still needs to do the Counting Jar?") or about issues the students would like to bring up.

4 SESSION FOLLOW-UP

Practice

Student Math Handbook Flip Chart: Use the *Student Math Handbook Flip Chart* pages 20, 21, 22 to reinforce content from today's session. See pages 146–148 in the back of this unit.

Eyes at Home

Math Focus Points

- Counting and keeping track of quantities
- Working with two-to-one correspondence
- Counting by groups of 2
- Making a representation of a set of data

Today's Plan		Materials
ACTIVITY 1 Introducing Eyes at Home	5 MIN CLASS	• *Student Activity Book,* p. 73 • Eyes at Home Sample Envelope*
MATH WORKSHOP 2 Counting Ones and Groups of Two 2A Eyes at Home 2B Counting Chairs 2C Pattern Block Grab 2D Counting Jar	15–25 MIN	2A • *Student Activity Book,* p. 73 • Students' completed Eyes at Home data 2B • Materials from Session 1.4, p. 43 2C • Materials from Session 1.2, p. 31 2D • Materials from Session 1.2, p. 31
DISCUSSION 3 Representing Handfuls	10 MIN CLASS	• *Student Activity Book,* p. 70 • Pattern blocks
SESSION FOLLOW-UP 4 Practice		• *Student Activity Book,* p. 74

*See *Materials to Prepare,* p. 23.

Classroom Routines

Attendance: What If We Start With . . . ? Count around the circle as usual to determine the total number of students present today. Then ask students what they think would happen if the count began with a different student and why. Choose a different student to start, count again, and discuss what happens.

ACTIVITY 1

Introducing Eyes at Home

Explain to students that during Math Workshop they will be counting the number of eyes in other people's homes using the homework from Session 1.3.

For the activity Eyes at Home, you will be looking at the number of eyes in other people's homes.

Direct students' attentions to *Student Activity Book* page 73 and read the headings, "Name on Envelope, Number of People, and Number of Eyes."

Here is an Eyes at Home envelope from my family. I made a card for myself, [my two sons and my daughter]. I also have a [cat], but since we are only counting people, I didn't include a card for my pet. How many people are there at my home?

Record your name and the rest of the information on *Student Activity Book* page 73.

So, we know I have [4] people in my home. How many *eyes* are there in my home?

Take suggestions and ask some students to show how they could count the eyes. Once children are sure of this number, record it in the appropriate place on *Student Activity Book* page 73. Explain to students that each of them should start by filling in his or her own information on the first row of the page.

Explain that the next step is to pick another student's family and determine how many people and how many eyes are in this student's family.

After you record your information, pick a different envelope. Record whose envelope you chose in this first column. Then count the number of people and the number of eyes in the envelope. As you work, remember to fill in the three pieces of data on the chart: the name on the envelope, the number of people counted, and the number of eyes counted.

Name Date

Sorting and Surveys

Eyes at Home

Choose an envelope. Count the number of people and the number of eyes. Record the data.

Name on Envelope	Number of People	Number of Eyes

© Pearson Education K

Session 1.5 Unit 7 73

▲ Student Activity Book, p. 73

MATH WORKSHOP

2 Counting Ones and Groups of Two

15–25 MIN

Explain that the following four activities are available during this Math Workshop and that today is the last day that Pattern Block Grab will be available. To prepare for the discussion at the end of this session, look through students' representations of their Pattern Block Grab and note a few different ways that students represented their data.

2A Eyes at Home

INDIVIDUALS

Students count the number of people and eyes in another student's home and record the numbers.

A student counts the number of eyes in another student's family.

ONGOING ASSESSMENT: Observing Students at Work

Students count items (eyes) that come in groups of 2 and show how they counted the items.

- **Do students accurately count the number of eyes?**
- **Do students count the eyes by 1s?** by 2s? Do they count all the left eyes and then the right eyes?
- **Do students notice any relationship/pattern between the number of people and the number of eyes?**

2B Counting Chairs

INDIVIDUALS

For complete details about this activity, see Session 1.4, page 44. See additional notes below.

DIFFERENTIATION: Supporting the Range of Learners

Extension For students who can easily figure out whether there are enough chairs for everyone in the class and explain how they know, pose new problems about the chairs in the class for them to solve. For example:

- If four new students joined the class, would we have enough chairs? How many more chairs would we need?
- What if six students were sick? How many extra chairs would we have?

Note whether students solve the problem starting from scratch or use the information they already have from solving the first problem.

2C Pattern Block Grab

INDIVIDUALS

For complete details about this activity, see Session 1.2, page 34.

2D Counting Jar

INDIVIDUALS

For complete details about this activity, see Session 1.2, page 35.

DISCUSSION

3 Representing Handfuls

10 MIN CLASS

Math Focus Points for Discussion

- Making a representation of a set of data

Ask students to turn to their completed *Student Activity Book* page 70 for this discussion. Bring a bin of pattern blocks and a copy of the page to the discussion.

When you did the Pattern Block Grab, you showed on *Student Activity Book* page 70 how many pattern blocks of each type you grabbed. What is one way you showed how many pattern blocks of each type you grabbed?

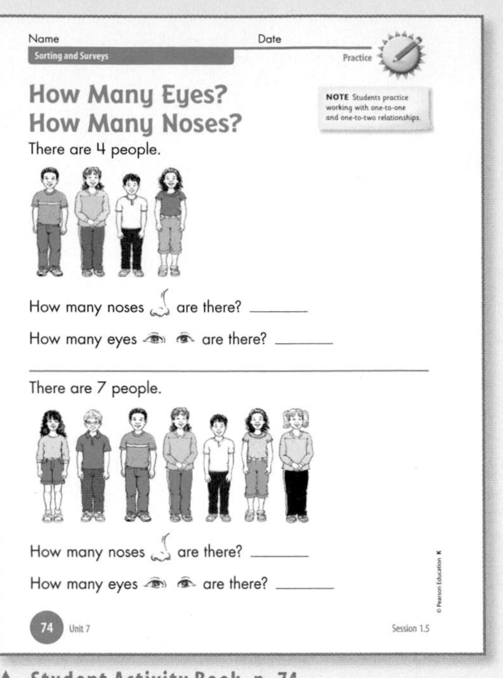

Name Date

Sorting and Surveys

Practice

How Many Eyes? How Many Noses?

NOTE Students practice working with one-to-one and one-to-two relationships.

There are 4 people.

How many noses are there? ______

How many eyes are there? ______

There are 7 people.

How many noses are there? ______

How many eyes are there? ______

© Pearson Education K

74 Unit 7 Session 1.5

▲ Student Activity Book, p. 74

I noticed that [Mary] drew every pattern block she grabbed. She drew all the hexagons together, all the triangles together, etc. Then she wrote how many of each underneath each group.

Can you tell how many of each pattern block she grabbed? . . . How many of each did she grab? . . . Did anyone else record in a similar way?

After students look closely at one representation, analyze the work of another student who represented his or her Pattern Block Grab data in a different way. Possible variations in recording: drawing one of each type of block and writing the number of that type next to the picture, writing the names of each type of block and the amount, or making a table that showed the data.

4 SESSION FOLLOW-UP
Practice

Practice: For reinforcement of this unit's content, have students complete *Student Activity Book* page 74.

Enough Chairs for the Class?

Math Focus Points

- Counting and keeping track of quantities
- Working with two-to-one correspondence
- Counting by groups of 2
- Using data to solve a problem

Today's Plan		Materials
1 MATH WORKSHOP **Counting Eyes and Chairs** 1A Eyes at Home 1B Counting Chairs 1C Counting Jar	20–35 MIN	1A • Materials from Session 1.5, p. 48 1B • Materials from Session 1.4, p. 43 1C • Materials from Session 1.2, p. 31
2 DISCUSSION **Enough Chairs for the Class?**	10 MIN CLASS	
3 SESSION FOLLOW-UP **Practice**		• *Student Math Handbook Flip Chart*, pp. 19, 20, 21, 22

Classroom Routines

Today's Question: Have you ever eaten corn on the cob? On chart paper, create a two-column table with the rows drawn in, titled "Have you ever eaten corn on the cob?" with "Yes" written at the top of one column and "No" written at the top of the other column. Students respond by writing their names in the appropriate column. As you discuss the results of the survey, ask students how the new table helps them count and compare the data.

1 MATH WORKSHOP

Counting Eyes and Chairs

Explain that the following three activities are available during this Math Workshop, and this is the last day for the Counting Jar.

1A Eyes at Home

For complete details about this activity, see Session 1.5, page 49.
See additional notes below.

DIFFERENTIATION: Supporting the Range of Learners

Extension Students who are easily counting the eyes in each home can try to figure out the number of eyes in all the students' homes.

Extension You might challange a few students to figure out how many fingers there are in some of the homes for which they have counted eyes.

1B Counting Chairs

For complete details about this activity, see Session 1.4, page 44.
See additional notes below.

1C Counting Jar

For complete details about this activity, see Session 1.2, page 35.

2 DISCUSSION

Enough Chairs for the Class?

Math Focus Points for Discussion

- Using data to solve a problem

Ask students to bring their work for Counting Chairs to this discussion.

For the Counting Chairs activity, you were asked to count how many chairs we have in the class. How many chairs do we have in the class?

If students came up with different numbers of chairs, record each answer on chart paper or on the board.

Counting the chairs in this class could be pretty challenging. There are a lot of them, and they are big so you can't really organize them to count them in the same way you can count cubes or pennies. How did you find out how many chairs we have in the class?

Ask students to share the methods they used to count. Emphasize students' strategies for keeping track of which chairs they counted and which chairs they still needed to count.

Next ask the students to share the strategies they used to decide whether there are enough chairs for everyone in the class.

There are [28] chairs in our class. Are there enough chairs for everyone in our class? . . . I notice that you used different ways to decide whether there are enough chairs for everyone in the class. [Emma] matched chairs and people. [Emma], can you show us what you did?

After each student shares his or her strategy, ask other students to raise their hands if they used the same strategy. This will allow students to be involved in the discussion without all the students sharing their strategies.

Ask two or three other students to share their strategies.

You all collected data on how many chairs there are in this class, but you did not all decide whether there were enough chairs for everyone in the class in the same way. There are many different ways to solve a problem like this.

3 SESSION FOLLOW-UP
Practice

Student Math Handbook Flip Chart: Use the *Student Math Handbook Flip Chart* pages 19, 20, 21, 22 to reinforce content from today's session. See pages 146–148 in the back of this unit.

INVESTIGATION 2

Mathematical Emphases

Data Analysis Sorting and classifying

Math Focus Points

- Comparing how objects are the same and different
- Using attributes to sort a set of objects
- Sorting a set of objects or data in different ways
- Identifying the attributes of an object
- Identifying an attribute that is common to several objects
- Grouping data into categories based on similar attributes

Data Analysis Carrying out a data investigation

Math Focus Points

- Interpreting results of a data investigation

How Are They the Same? How Are They Different?

Session	Student Activity Book	Student Math Handbook Flip Chart	Professional Development: Read Ahead of Time
SESSION 2.1 p. 62 **Self-Portraits** Students work together to sort people in the class by different attributes. Students create self-portraits that they will later sort according to common characteristics.		49	
SESSION 2.2 p. 69 **Attribute Match-Up** Students are reintroduced to *Attribute Match-Up*, an activity from *Who Is In School Today?* In this activity, students match up attribute blocks that have at least one characteristic in common.		47	• **Teacher Note:** Sorting and Classifying, p. 129
SESSION 2.3 p. 75 **Boxes, Bottles, and Cans** Students are introduced to Boxes, Bottles, and Cans in which they sort a set of containers according to one attribute. Math Workshop focuses on identifying and comparing attributes. The session ends with a discussion about how two objects are the same and different.	75	48	
SESSION 2.4 p. 81 **Same and Different** Math Workshop focuses on comparing attributes and sorting by attributes. Students have another discussion about same and different as they compare two objects.		48	• **Dialogue Box:** How Are These Coats the Same and Different?, p. 141

Classroom Routines See page 16 for an overview.

Calendar
- Class calendar

Patterns on the Pocket Chart
- Pocket Chart(s) or Sentence Pocket Chart
- Question Mark Cards (from Investigation 1)
- Prepared cups or bags of pattern blocks (1 per pair)
- Prepared cups or bags of square tiles (1 per pair)

Attendance
- Attendance Stick

Today's Question
- *Today's Question* chart for Session 2.4. See instructions on page 81.

Materials to Gather	Materials to Prepare
• **Chart paper** • **Drawing materials: crayons, markers, color pencils** • **Mirrors** (as needed; optional)	• **Containers** Collect 8–10 of each of the following containers for Session 2.3: small boxes, empty plastic bottles, and unopened cans. You might ask students to contribute containers from home. Put each type of container in a separate box or bag.
• **Students' completed self-portraits** (from Session 2.1) • **Materials for Eyes at Home** See Session 1.5.	• **M8, Assessment Checklist: Sorting** ✓ Make copies. (3–4 per class, plus extra as needed) • **Attribute blocks** (half or whole set per pair) Either use whole sets or divide each set in half so you have four sets. If you do divide them, make one set of thin blocks and one of thick, thus eliminating thickness as a possible attribute.
• **Materials for Sorting Portraits** See Session 2.1. • **Materials for *Attribute Match-Up*** See Session 2.2.	• **M8, Assessment Checklist: Sorting** ✓ (from Session 2.2) • **Containers** Organize the containers you collected into 3 sets: 8–10 boxes, 8–10 cans, and 8–10 bottles. The containers within each set should be varied to allow for sorting in different ways. Put each set into a larger box or bag. • **Chart paper** Title a chart "Comparing Boxes." Make two columns and label one "Same" and the other "Different." • **Boxes** Find two boxes with some obvious similar attributes and some different attributes.
• **Materials for Boxes, Bottles, and Cans** See Session 2.3. • **Materials for Sorting Portraits** See Session 2.1. • **Materials for *Attribute Match-Up*** See Session 2.2.	• **2 Objects to Compare** Find two similar objects that have noticeable differences, such as two different shoes, two books, or a wooden and a plastic block. • **Chart paper** Title a chart "Comparing [Shoes]." Put in the name of the objects you have chosen to compare. Make two columns and label one "Same" and the other "Different." • **M9–M10, Family Letter** Make copies. (1 per student)

✓ Checklist Available

How Are They the Same? How Are They Different?, *continued*

	Student Activity Book	Student Math Handbook Flip Chart	Professional Development: Read Ahead of Time	
SESSION 2.5 p. 84				
Attribute Dominoes Students learn *Attribute Dominoes*, a game in which students take turns making a train of attribute blocks by placing blocks next to each other that have at least one attribute in common. Math Workshop continues to focus on identifying and comparing attributes.		47, 48, 49		
SESSION 2.6 p. 88				
Favorite Lunch Foods Students provide data about their favorite lunch foods. As a class they organize the data in different ways and discuss what they notice about the data.	76		• **Dialogue Box:** Is a Peach Dessert or Not?, p. 143	

Materials to Gather	Materials to Prepare
• **Attribute blocks** • **Opaque bags** (paper or plastic; 1 per pair) • **Materials for Boxes, Bottles, and Cans** See Session 2.3. • **Materials for Sorting Portraits** See Session 2.1.	
• **Children's literature about lunch** Options include *This is the Way We Eat Our Lunch: A Book About Children Around the World* by Edith Baer, *Lunch* by Denise Fleming, and *School Lunch* by True Kelley (optional) • **5″ x 7″ index cards** (1 per student) • **Drawing materials** (as needed) • **Glue stick or tape** (1)	• **Chart or butcher paper** Make a lunch data chart by taping chart or butcher paper together. See page 95.

Self-Portraits

Math Focus Points

- Comparing how objects are the same and different
- Using attributes to sort a set of objects
- Sorting a set of objects or data in different ways

Today's Plan		Materials
ACTIVITY **1 Sorting People**	10–15 MIN · CLASS	• Chart paper
ACTIVITY **2 Creating Self-Portraits**	15–25 MIN · INDIVIDUALS	• Drawing materials such as crayons, markers, color pencils; mirrors (optional)
ACTIVITY **3 Introducing Sorting Portraits**	5 MIN · CLASS	• Students' completed self-portraits (from Activity 2)
SESSION FOLLOW-UP **4 Practice**		• *Student Math Handbook Flip Chart*, p. 49

Classroom Routines

Calendar: What's Missing? **Remove five dates on the monthly calendar. Challenge students to tell you which cards are missing and how they know.**

1 ACTIVITY

Sorting People

10–15 MIN CLASS

Introduce this activity by choosing a characteristic that is visually obvious about some of the students in your classroom. It might be a physical characteristic such as "has brown hair," or it might be something about their clothes, such as "long sleeves."

I noticed today that there is something the same about some of you, but not everyone. Some people are [wearing sneakers] today. Let's see how many people are [wearing sneakers].

Ask all the students who are [wearing sneakers] to stand next to you. The rest of the students should remain seated. If there are any students who are not sure whether they meet your rule, discuss it as a class.

These people are all [wearing sneakers]. Let's count them. So there are [eight] people [wearing sneakers]. If we describe this group as the [Wearing Sneakers] Group, what can we say about the people who are not standing next to me?

Students may name some of the characteristics of some of the group that does not fit your rule, such as that they are wearing brown shoes, sandals, and so on.

So we can make other groups like [brown shoes and sandals]. Is there something we can say is the same about everyone who is not standing next to me? . . . We could also call this group People Who Are [Not Wearing Sneakers] or People [Wearing Other Kinds of Shoes].

Ask the students to look carefully at their classmates to see if they can find something else some students have in common, but not all the students. Ask a student who noticed something to whisper it in your ear. Be sensitive to any physical attribute that might make a child feel singled out or uncomfortable.

[Carmen] says that she noticed some people have brown hair. Can the students who have brown hair stand next to me? . . . How many students are there with brown hair? . . . What can we say about the people not standing next to me?①

Teaching Note

① **Language and Sorting** Identifying attributes and describing what is the same about a group of people or objects includes a significant language component. Often, students can sort objects correctly because they can visually identify a common attribute but have difficulty naming the attribute or naming the group as a whole. The activities in this Investigation include many opportunities to use language to describe attributes and to discuss what is the same and different about sets of objects and data.

As you sorted people in this class, you noticed some ways some people were the same today and the ways some people were different. You were paying attention to people's characteristics or attributes. You noticed [the kinds of shoes people were wearing] and [their hair color].

Some students are sorted into two groups, people wearing sneakers and people who are not wearing sneakers.

Explain that today students will look closely at themselves and make self-portraits that show what they look like. Tell them that later they will be sorting these portraits just as they sorted the people in the class.

Be sure to put lots of details in your picture. What attributes do you think you should include in your portrait so we can tell it is you?

Students will probably list characteristics that are specific to themselves. Help them think about what general attribute they are describing.

[Rebecca] said she should make sure she includes her brown curly hair. I agree. Everyone should show their hair color and whether their hair is straight or curly. What other attributes are important to include in your portraits?

Make a chart of the attributes that students say are important to include. Add to the list any important attributes you think are missing. Important attributes to include are hair color, short/long hair, curly/straight hair, eye color, skin color, other special things like glasses or missing teeth. Ask the students to draw themselves in the clothes they are wearing that day.

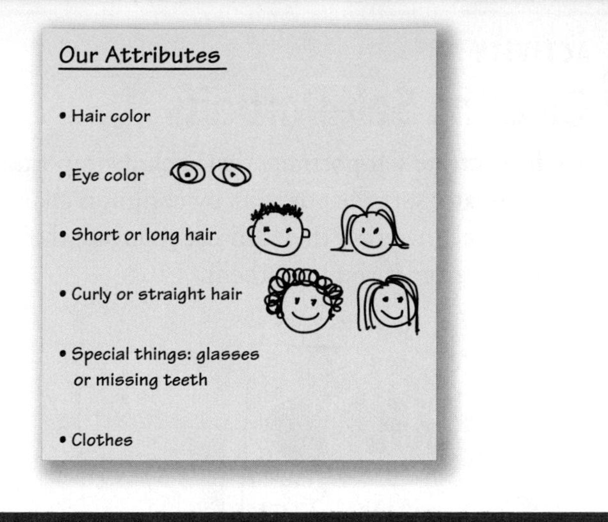

ONGOING ASSESSMENT: Observing Students at Work

Students sort themselves into groups using a designated attribute.

- **Are students able to determine whether or not they have the identified attribute?**
- **Are they able to sort themselves into the correct group?**

DIFFERENTIATION: Supporting the Range of Learners

ELL English Language Learners may need help understanding and using descriptive words in this activity. You can review the relevant vocabulary with them in context as they work on their self-portraits in the next activity.

When I look at Mia's and Kiyo's portraits, I see they both have *long* hair. Mia's hair is *curly,* but Kiyo's is straight.

Use gestures to highlight specific attributes as you describe them. You can also review the names of colors and types of clothing, as well as words that describe the patterns on children's clothes (i.e., striped, solid, polka-dotted).

ACTIVITY

2 Creating Self-Portraits

15–25 MIN INDIVIDUALS

Students create self-portraits that include important attributes so that they can later sort the portraits by common characteristics. Show students the materials they can use to create their self-portraits. They can use mirrors if you have them.

Sample Student Work

Sample Student Work

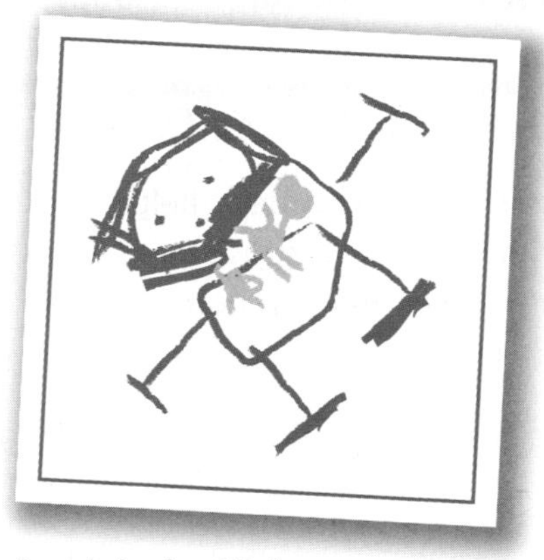

Sample Student Work

Sample Student Work

Sample Student Work

Sample Student Work

ONGOING ASSESSMENT: Observing Students at Work

Students identify and draw important attributes in portraits of themselves.

- **Can students identify important attributes to include in their portraits (e.g., eye color, hair color, clothes)?**

ACTIVITY

3 Introducing Sorting Portraits

Gather students in a circle with seven or eight portraits in the center. Identify one attribute that several portraits share.

As I was looking at your self-portraits, I noticed some things that are the same about some of the pictures. For example, the people in three of these portraits are [wearing shorts]. Let's see if we can put these portraits into two groups. One group will be the people who are [Wearing Shorts] and the other will be the people who are [Not Wearing Shorts].

With the students' help, sort the pictures into two mutually exclusive groups (one group having the attribute, one group NOT having the attribute).

Students sort their portraits.

It is likely that some portraits will not clearly be able to be sorted into two groups. Ask students for their ideas about what to do with these pictures. They may suggest putting the pictures in a third group—a Can't Tell group. As you sort the pictures, place them side-by-side, so that the chosen attribute remains visible.

After sorting the portraits once as a whole group, help the class brainstorm some other characteristics they could use for sorting when they work in small groups. Give examples that involve more than two possible categories, such as eye color, hair color, and types of shirts (e.g., stripes, solid, prints).

Here's another way I could sort the pictures, this time using more than two groups. I am going to sort them into groups using [the shirts people are wearing]. What kinds of [shirts are people wearing]?

Again, sort the pictures into groups, using [the kinds of shirts] that students suggest. Point out that this time, you have several categories, rather than just two. You might again have a Can't Tell group.

Explain that students can use any of these and other ideas for sorting portraits in their small groups during Math Workshop for the next few days.

SESSION FOLLOW-UP

4 Practice

Student Math Handbook Flip Chart: Use the *Student Math Handbook Flip Chart* page 49 to reinforce content from today's session. See pages 146–148 in the back of this unit.

Attribute Match-Up

Math Focus Points

- Identifying the attributes of an object
- Identifying an attribute that is common to several objects
- Comparing how objects are the same and different

Vocabulary

attributes

Today's Plan			Materials
1 ACTIVITY **Reintroducing *Attribute Match-Up***	5–10 MIN	CLASS	• Attribute blocks*
2 MATH WORKSHOP **Matching and Sorting** 2A *Attribute Match-Up* 2B Sorting Portraits 2C Eyes at Home	20–30 MIN		2A • Attribute blocks* 2B • M8* ☑ • Students' completed self-portraits (from Session 2.1) 2C • Materials from Session 1.5, p. 48
3 DISCUSSION **Checking In**	5 MIN	CLASS	
4 SESSION FOLLOW-UP **Practice**			• *Student Math Handbook Flip Chart,* p. 47

*See *Materials to Prepare,* p. 59.

Classroom Routines

Patterns on the Pocket Chart: What Comes Here? Arrange an ABB repeating pattern on the first two rows of the pocket chart using 14 or more pattern blocks (green triangle, yellow hexagon, yellow hexagon). Cover the 8th through the last pattern block with Question Mark Cards. Follow the basic *Patterns* activity but instead of asking for the *next* pattern block in the pattern sequence, point to the 12th pocket and ask students what pattern block is under the question mark card. Students hold up the pattern block they think it is.

Teaching Notes

➊ **Attribute Blocks** Attribute blocks are a set of blocks that vary by color, shape, size and thickness. Students should be familiar with attribute blocks, as they were used in the *Who Is In School Today?* and more recently in the geometry unit *Make a Shape, Make a Block*.

➋ **But They're Different!** Paying attention to just one attribute can be challenging for young students. Matching two objects that are exactly the same will be easy for most students, but some students have difficulty seeing that two objects with only one attribute the same have something in common. For example, students may say that a small red circle and a big blue circle do not have anything in common because they are two different colors and two different sizes. See the Differentiation: Supporting the Range of Learners section (page 72) for more information on how to help students with this idea.

ACTIVITY

1 Reintroducing *Attribute Match-Up*

5–10 MIN CLASS

Spread out the attribute blocks so all the students can see them.➊

In the next few weeks, we are going to do some activities with these attribute blocks. What do you notice about the attribute blocks?

Students might say:

"The blocks are different colors."

"I see circles!"

"Some are big. Some are small."

Yes, the blocks are different colors and different shapes and different sizes. Color, shape, and size are some of the **attributes** of these blocks.

Hold up a red, large circle (thick or thin).

How would you describe the attributes of this block?

After students describe the first block, ask them to compare it to the other blocks.

Can you find another block that has at least one attribute that is the same as this block? It doesn't have to be exactly the same as the other block—there just has to be at least one way that the two blocks are the same.

As students hold up two attribute blocks with at least one attribute in common, ask them to describe how they are the same.➋

Today during Math Workshop you are going to play a game called *Attribute Match-Up,* which you played at the beginning of the year. In this game you are going to look for two blocks that match. Two blocks match when they have at least one thing or attribute that is the same.

Hold up one block and ask students to raise their hands if they see another block that is the same in one particular way. As students make matches, ask them to describe how the blocks match.

If two students come up with different matches for the same block, ask students if it is possible to have two matches for the same block. If the idea that there can be two matches for the same block does not come up, bring it up yourself. Some students may have difficulty with the idea that there can be more than one match for one block.❸

Students find pairs of attribute blocks with at least one attribute that is the same.

Pay attention to whether students are focusing on different attributes to make matches or only one. If students are only focusing on, for example, color, give students an example of two blocks that match by an attribute other than color and ask if they match.

Take a look at these two shapes [large red circle/large blue circle]. Could these two shapes be a match? Why?

MATH WORKSHOP

Matching and Sorting

20–30 MIN

Explain that three activities are available during Math Workshop and today is the last day that the Eyes at Home activity will be available.

Teaching Note

❸ **Keep the Sets Together** Remind students that these blocks are different from other materials they have used because the sets cannot be divided. They need to remain as a whole set in order to be able to compare likenesses and differences in the attributes highlighted by the set.

Teaching Note

❹ **Assessing Students as They Sort** By the end of this unit, students are expected to be able to sort a set of objects according to their attributes (Benchmark 3). This means that they identify attributes of an object, name how two different objects are the same, and group together objects that are the same according to one attribute. Use Assessment Checklist: Sorting (M8) to keep track of your observations of students sorting objects over the course of this Investigation and unit.

Professional Development

❺ **Teacher Note:** Sorting and Classifying, p. 129

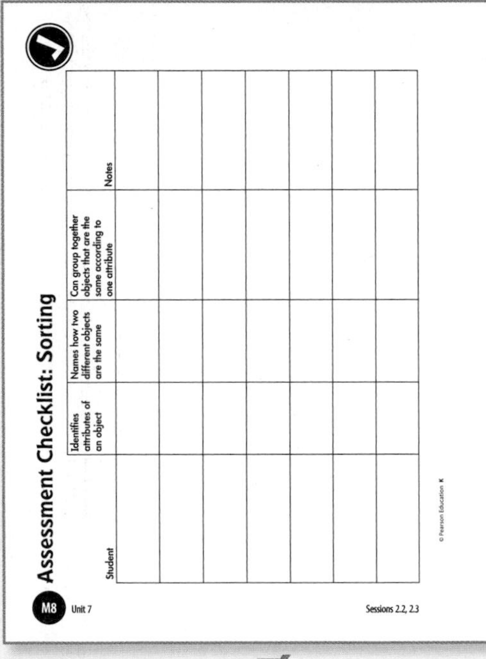

Assessment Checklist: Sorting

Student	Identifies attributes of an object	Names how two different objects are the same	Can group together objects that are the same according to one attribute	Notes

© Pearson Education K

M8 Unit 7 Sessions 2.2, 2.3

▲ Resource Masters, M8

PAIRS

2A Attribute Match-Up

Students work in pairs to match attribute blocks that have at least one attribute that is the same.

Two pairs or four pairs can play *Attribute Match-Up* depending on whether you have divided the attribute blocks sets in half.

ONGOING ASSESSMENT: Observing Students at Work

Students identify attributes and think about attributes that are common to several objects.

- **Can students identify the different attributes of the attribute blocks?** Do they recognize that they vary by color, size, shape (and thickness)?
- **Are students able to match blocks with at least one common attribute?** Are they able to identify how they are similar?
- **Do students match blocks by looking only for one attribute (e.g., they only match blocks by color) or do they look for a variety of similar attributes (e.g., sometimes they match by color, other times by shape)?**

DIFFERENTIATION: Supporting the Range of Learners

Intervention Some students may have difficulty focusing on only one attribute at a time. They may think that two blocks do not match unless they are almost completely the same. Help students focus on single attributes by asking them the following questions:

- How would you describe this block? . . . You said this block is a [circle]. Can you find another block that matches that attribute? Can you find another block that is a [circle], but is not [red]?

PAIRS GROUPS

2B Sorting Portraits

Students sort the class set of self-portraits in different ways according to different attributes. Depending on the number of students in your class, you may want to divide the set of portraits into two sets and have students work in groups of two or three.❹❺

ONGOING ASSESSMENT: Observing Students at Work

Students sort objects in different ways according to their attributes.

- **Are students able to create a sorting strategy that involves two mutually exclusive groups (e.g., has an attribute, does *not* have an attribute)?**
- **Are students able to create a sorting strategy that involves multiple groups?** If so, do they choose a characteristic (e.g., hair color) and stick with it, or do they switch to different attributes as they complete their sort?
- **Do students notice that pictures can be sorted in multiple ways?** For example, a portrait that appears in the Shorts group for one sort, might also be placed in a Brown Hair group for a hair-color sort.

Assessment Checklist: Sorting

Student	Identifies attributes of an object	Names how two different objects are the same	Can group together objects that are the same according to one attribute	Notes
Carmen Portraits	"I'm going to do eyes"		sorts portraits accurately by eye color	
Kaitlyn Attribute Match-Up	describes blocks as blue	puts 2 blocks tog. says both are squares		
Jae Attribute Match-Up	only names colors	matches yellow & blue triangles can't say how they are the same		difficulty describing but can sort
Lisa Portraits			only sorts by shirt color	says they are all different, observe in another activity

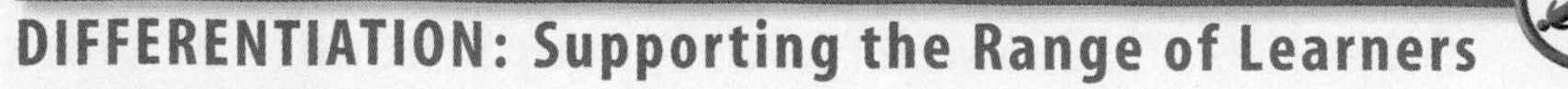

DIFFERENTIATION: Supporting the Range of Learners

Intervention Students may have difficulty focusing on one way that a group of portraits are the same. For example, they may make a group and say the portraits in the group have curly hair and straight hair. Ask these students to point out all the portraits that have straight hair and put those in one group. Help them label the group according to the one characteristic that is the same.

2C Eyes at Home

For complete details about this activity, see Session 1.5, page 49.

3 DISCUSSION
Checking In

Use this time to discuss the Counting Jar activity, finished in Session 1.6. Count the pattern blocks in the jar. If any students used the pairs of pattern blocks to figure out the total, ask them to share their strategies for this. Ask a few students to share how they represented the contents of the jar.

4 SESSION FOLLOW-UP
Practice

Student Math Handbook Flip Chart: Use the *Student Math Handbook Flip Chart* page 47 to reinforce content from today's session. See pages 146–148 in the back of this unit.

Boxes, Bottles, and Cans

Math Focus Points

- Identifying the attributes of an object
- Using attributes to sort a set of objects
- Comparing how objects are the same and different

Vocabulary

comparing
same
different

Today's Plan			Materials
1 ACTIVITY **Introducing Boxes, Bottles, and Cans**	5–10 MIN	CLASS	• Containers*
2 MATH WORKSHOP **Sorting Portraits and Containers** 2A Boxes, Bottles, and Cans 2B Sorting Portraits 2C *Attribute Match-Up*	15–25 MIN		2A • M8 (from Session 2.2) • Containers* 2B • Materials from Session 2.1, p. 62 2C • Materials from Session 2.2, p. 69
3 DISCUSSION **Same and Different Containers**	10 MIN	CLASS	• Chart: "Comparing Boxes"*; 2 boxes • *Student Math Handbook Flip Chart,* p. 48
4 SESSION FOLLOW-UP **Practice**			• *Student Activity Book,* p. 75

*See *Materials to Prepare,* p. 59.

Classroom Routines

Attendance: Comparing Groups Count around the circle as usual, and then count the number of students present in class and the number absent from class today. Ask students if there are more students present or more students absent. Use the Attendance Stick to represent the situation and to model students' strategies. Challenge students to figure out how many more and discuss their strategies.

Professional Development

① **Teacher Note:** Sorting and Classifying, p. 129

ACTIVITY

5–10 MIN CLASS

1 Introducing Boxes, Bottles, and Cans

Show students the sets of boxes, bottles, and cans you have prepared. If students have contributed to these sets, acknowledge their help.

We've been collecting lots of different containers to use during math time. I put each kind of container in a separate bag. That's one way that these things can be sorted: [point to each set in turn] boxes, bottles, and cans.

Today during Math Workshop, you and a partner can choose one of these sets to work with. You'll be making two groups; one group that has something special about it, and one that does *not* have this special thing or attribute. For example, I'm going to sort the bottles. I'm going to make two groups and the attribute that I'm choosing is [white]. I'll put all the [white] bottles in one group, and the rest of the bottles in another group. This is the group of [white] bottles, and this is the group of [not white] bottles.

Count the bottles in each group and then count the total number of bottles. Point out to students that every bottle in the collection is in a group and that there are no leftovers.

Students sort bottles into two groups such as White and Not White.

Mix up the bottles again and spread them out so that students can see them. Take suggestions for sorting, using a Not group.①

Who has a different suggestion for how we can sort the bottles into two groups, using Not as one of the groups?

Because thinking about a Not group can be challenging for some students, you may need to help students clarify the language they use to describe each group.

Explain to students that during Math Workshop, they can work with a partner on this activity. After sorting one collection of objects in at least two ways they can switch collections with another pair of students.

MATH WORKSHOP

15–25 MIN

Sorting Portraits and Containers

Explain that the following three activities are available during Math Workshop. Students will continue with these Math Workshop activities in Session 2.4.

2A Boxes, Bottles, and Cans

Students sort sets of containers into two groups according to one attribute. They sort the set of containers in at least two ways before moving on to sort another set or do another activity.❷

ONGOING ASSESSMENT: Observing Students at Work

Students sort objects into two groups according to their attributes.

- **Are students able to sort the objects into two groups, one being a Not group?**
- **Can students sort the items in more than one way?**
- **Can students verbalize their reasons for grouping objects together?**

DIFFERENTIATION: Supporting the Range of Learners

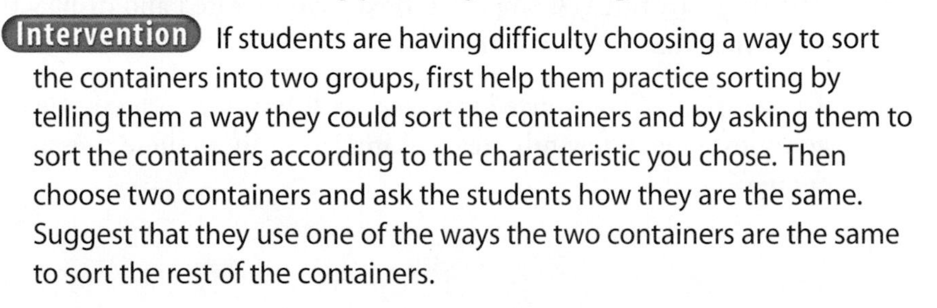

Intervention If students are having difficulty choosing a way to sort the containers into two groups, first help them practice sorting by telling them a way they could sort the containers and by asking them to sort the containers according to the characteristic you chose. Then choose two containers and ask the students how they are the same. Suggest that they use one of the ways the two containers are the same to sort the rest of the containers.

Teaching Note

❷ **Assessing Students as They Sort** By the end of this unit, students are expected to be able to sort a set of objects according to their attributes (Benchmark 3). This means that they identify attributes of an object, name how two different objects are the same, and group together objects that are the same according to one attribute. Use Assessment Checklist: Sorting (M8), to keep track of your observations of students sorting objects over the course of this Investigation and unit.

Intervention Students may have difficulty labeling one group as Not. It is challenging for young students to think of attributes of objects in the negative. It is hard to think of a box that is red as not being green. Ask students to first sort all of the boxes that are [green] into one group, then ask how the remaining boxes are the same.

2B Sorting Portraits

For complete details about this activity, see Session 2.1, page 67.

DIFFERENTIATION: Supporting the Range of Learners

Extension Once students have sorted the portraits in a number of ways, some of the students may be interested in recording data about the class based on their sorts. For example, they might record how many people have brown eyes, how many people have blue eyes, and how many people have other-colored eyes.

2C *Attribute Match-Up*

For complete details about this activity, see Session 2.2, page 70.

DIFFERENTIATION: Supporting the Range of Learners

Extension Suggest to students who easily find matches to the attribute blocks that they select one block from the set and find all the possible matches to that one block.

3 DISCUSSION Same and Different Containers

Math Focus Points for Discussion

- Comparing how objects are the same and different

Post the chart titled "Comparing Boxes" you created and display the two boxes that you chose ahead of time.

Today, some of you started working with boxes like these. We are going to spend a few minutes looking carefully at these two boxes and comparing them.

Hold up one box.

If you wanted to tell someone about this box but the person couldn't see it, what would you tell the person?

Students might say:

"It's a big square box."

"The box is blue with some letters on the side."

Now let's look at both of these boxes. How are they the same?

On the chart, write down all the ways the students say the containers are the same.

Now let's think about how they are different.

Again list how the boxes are different. Students may find making a list of how objects are different more challenging than making a list of how they are the same. If this is the case, prompt them by asking questions about particular characteristics:

- This one has a top; does the other one?
- What is the shape of this one like? How about the other one?

Comparing Boxes	
Same	**Different**
Both are rectangles. Both have white. Both have writing. Both have 6 faces.	One is small; one is large. One has red; one has blue. One is for eating; the other one isn't. One has pictures; the other doesn't.

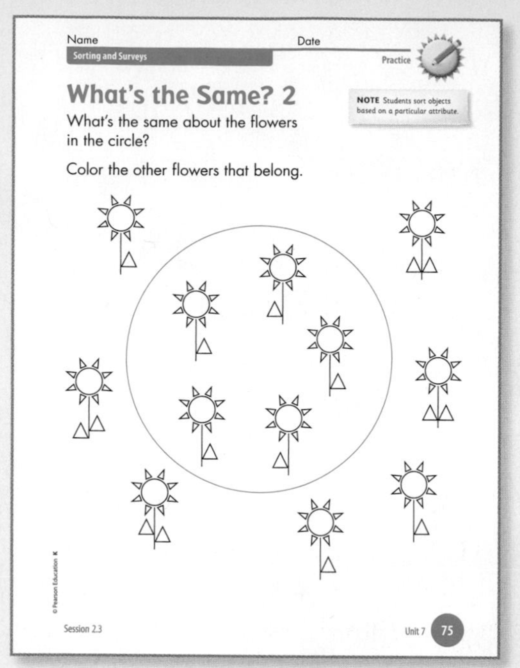

Name Date

Sorting and Surveys

Practice

What's the Same? 2

NOTE Students sort objects based on a particular attribute.

What's the same about the flowers in the circle?

Color the other flowers that belong.

© Pearson Education K

Session 2.3 Unit 7 75

▲ Student Activity Book, p. 75

Review the list with the students. End the discussion by helping the students think about how making these lists might help them with the Bottle, Boxes, and Cans activity.

We came up with many ways that these two boxes are the same and are different. When you are doing the Boxes, Bottles, and Cans activity, you might think of using some of the ideas on our list as ways to sort the containers.

SESSION FOLLOW-UP

4 Practice

Practice: For reinforcement of this unit's content, have students complete *Student Activity Book* page 75.

Student Math Handbook Flip Chart: Use the *Student Math Handbook Flip Chart* page 48 to reinforce concepts from today's session.

SESSION 2.4

Same and Different

Math Focus Points

- Comparing how objects are the same and different
- Using attributes to sort a set of objects
- Sorting a set of objects or data in different ways

Vocabulary

describe

Today's Plan		Materials
1 MATH WORKSHOP **Sorting Portraits and Containers** 1A Boxes, Bottles, and Cans; 1B Sorting Portraits; 1C *Attribute Match-Up*	20–35 MIN	1A • Materials from Session 2.3, p. 75 1B • Materials from Session 2.1, p. 62 1C • Materials from Session 2.2, p. 69
2 DISCUSSION **Same and Different**	10 MIN CLASS	• 2 objects to compare*; chart: "Comparing [Shoes]"*
3 SESSION FOLLOW-UP **Homework**		• *Student Math Handbook Flip Chart,* p. 48 • M9–M10, Family Letter*

*See *Materials to Prepare,* p. 59.

Classroom Routines

Today's Question: Would you rather be a teacher or a doctor when you grow up?

On chart paper, create a horizontal table titled "Would you rather be a teacher or a doctor when you grow up?" with the label "Teacher" written at the left of one row and "Doctor" written at the left of the other row. Students respond by writing their names in the appropriate row. As you discuss the results of the survey, continue to ask about and experiment with different ways to organize the data so that it is easier to tell which group has more.

Professional Development

➊ **Dialogue Box:** How Are These Coats the Same and Different?, p. 141

MATH WORKSHOP

20–35 MIN

Sorting Portraits and Containers

Explain that the following three activities are available during Math Workshop and that today is the last day *Attribute Match-Up* will be available.

1A Boxes, Bottles, and Cans

For complete details about this activity, see Session 2.3, page 76.

DIFFERENTIATION: Supporting the Range of Learners

Extension Students may be interested in trying to sort the containers into more than two groups.

1B Sorting Portraits

For complete details about this activity, see Session 2.1, page 67.

1C *Attribute Match-Up*

For complete details about this activity, see Session 2.2, page 70.

DISCUSSION

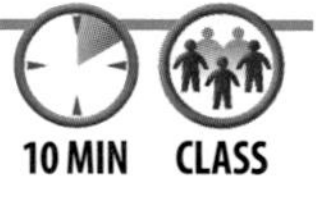

Same and Different

Math Focus Points for Discussion

- Comparing how objects are the same and different

Post the chart titled "Same and Different" you have created for this discussion and display the two objects you chose to compare. Have a similar discussion to the one during the previous session in which you compared two boxes.➊

Choose one object to describe.

If you wanted to describe this [shoe] to someone who cannot see it, how would you describe it?

Here is another [shoe]. How are these two [shoes] the same?

Write down all the ways students say the two shoes are the same.

How are these two [shoes] different?

Write down all of the ways students say that the two shoes (or whatever you are comparing) are different.

Students discuss the ways the two shoes are the same and different.

SESSION FOLLOW-UP

Homework

Student Math Handbook Flip Chart: Use the *Student Math Handbook Flip Chart* page 48 to reinforce concepts from today's session.

Family Letter: Send home copies of the Family Letter (M9–M10) with each student.

SESSION 2.5

Attribute Dominoes

Math Focus Points

- Comparing how objects are the same and different
- Using attributes to sort a set of objects
- Sorting a set of objects or data in different ways

Today's Plan		Materials
1 ACTIVITY **Introducing *Attribute Dominoes***	5 MIN CLASS	• Attribute blocks • Opaque bags
2 MATH WORKSHOP **Attribute Matching and Sorting** 2A *Attribute Dominoes* 2B Boxes, Bottles, and Cans 2C Sorting Portraits	20–35 MIN	2A • Attribute blocks; opaque bags 2B • Materials from Session 2.3, p. 75 2C • Materials from Session 2.1, p. 62
3 DISCUSSION **Checking In**	5 MIN CLASS	
4 SESSION FOLLOW-UP **Practice**		• *Student Math Handbook Flip Chart,* pp. 47, 48, 49

Classroom Routines

Calendar: Mixed Up Calendar Choose two date cards and change their position on the calendar so that they are out of order. Challenge students to find the mistakes and help you fix them.

ACTIVITY

1 Introducing Attribute Dominoes

Tell students that during Math Workshop they are going to play a new game with the attribute blocks. Choose a student to demonstrate the game with you. Ask the student to draw five blocks from the opaque bag of attribute blocks. Then do the same yourself. Pick one more block from the bag and lay it in the middle between you.

I have five blocks, and [Rebecca] has five blocks. First I am going to look at my blocks and see if I have a block that matches at least one of the attributes of this block in the middle here.

If you have a block that matches, lay it down next to the block in the middle. Say how your block matches.

My block matches this block because both of them are [yellow].

Draw a new block out of the bag to replace the one you matched. Then it is your partner's turn.

Now it is [Rebecca's] turn. There are now two blocks to make matches with. [Rebecca] is going to look at her blocks to see if she has a block that matches either of the blocks. Does she have a block that matches either one of these? Remember that blocks match if they have one or more attributes that are the same.

If your partner has a match, your partner places the block next to the block it matches, creating a train of blocks. Your partner says how the two blocks match and then draws a new block to replace the one he or she put down.

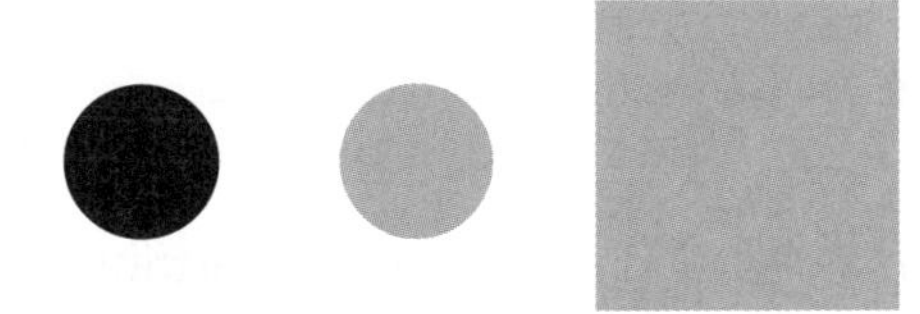

Explain to students that they continue taking turns matching blocks. As the "train" of blocks grows, players may choose a block at either end to match (players cannot match a block in the middle of the train). If a player is stuck and can find no matches, she or he may draw a new block.

Continue to play until all of the blocks are put in the train or you can't find any more matches among any of the blocks.①

Teaching Note

① There Are Other Ways That the Blocks Match When a player describes how they see that the two blocks match, the other player may notice other ways that they match. Encourage the players to share other ways that the blocks match.

20–35 MIN

2 MATH WORKSHOP

Attribute Matching and Sorting

Explain that the following three activities are available during Math Workshop. The first two activities continue into Investigation 3.

PAIRS

2A *Attribute Dominoes*

Students play dominoes with a set of attribute blocks. They make a train by putting a block down next to another block if the blocks have at least one attribute in common. They keep playing until they run out of blocks that will match the blocks at either end of the train.

Students play Attribute Dominoes, *making a train of attribute blocks by laying blocks next to each other if they have at least one common attribute.*

ONGOING ASSESSMENT: Observing Students at Work

Students match objects with common attributes

- **Do students identify blocks from their collection, which have attributes that match the block on the table?**
- **Do students use size, shape, color, and thickness as attributes that can be matched, or do they focus on only one or two of these attributes?**
- **Can students verbalize the attribute that they are matching?**

DIFFERENTIATION: Supporting the Range of Learners

Intervention Students who have difficulty identifying common attributes between the few blocks in their "hand" and the blocks on the table can continue to play *Attribute Match-Up* instead.

ELL Some English Language Learners might need additional reinforcement to follow the rules of this game. You can check in with them during Math Workshop and review the rules as necessary. Think aloud as you take a few turns with each student, emphasizing key vocabulary words such as *attribute, match, both, either,* and *same.* Encourage students to think aloud as they continue playing the game with their partners.

2B Boxes, Bottles, and Cans

PAIRS GROUPS

For complete details about this activity, see Session 2.3, page 76.

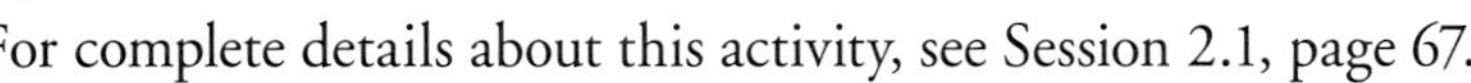

2C Sorting Portraits

PAIRS GROUPS

For complete details about this activity, see Session 2.1, page 67.

3 DISCUSSION
Checking In

5 MIN CLASS

Take this opportunity to discuss any issues that you noticed while observing students at work. The topic might be mathematical in nature, such as a strategy you would like all students to consider or a common error or misconception you would like students to discuss. The issue might also be logistical, such as clarifying the steps to a game, or management related, for example, noise level or working with a partner.

Other alternatives include checking in with students about which activities they worked on, asking everyone to hold up a piece of work, or allowing students to raise a question or make a comment about today's math class.

4 SESSION FOLLOW-UP
Practice

Student Math Handbook Flip Chart: Use the *Student Math Handbook Flip Chart* pages 47, 48, 49 to reinforce content from today's session. See pages 146–148 in the back of this unit.

SESSION 2.6

Favorite Lunch Foods

Math Focus Points

- Grouping data into categories based on similar attributes
- Sorting a set of objects or data in different ways
- Interpreting results of a data investigation

Today's Plan		Materials
ACTIVITY **1 Introducing the Lunch Food Data Activity**	5–10 MIN, CLASS	• Children's literature about lunch (optional)
ACTIVITY **2 Generating Lunch Food Data**	15–20 MIN, INDIVIDUALS, PAIRS	• 5″ x 7″ index cards; drawing materials
DISCUSSION **3 Sorting Favorite Lunch Food Data**	10–15 MIN, CLASS	• Students' lunch data cards (from Activity 2); glue stick or tape; chart: lunch data*
SESSION FOLLOW-UP **4 Practice**		• *Student Activity Book*, p. 76

*See *Materials to Prepare,* p. 61.

Classroom Routines

Patterns on the Pocket Chart: What Comes Here? Arrange an AAB repeating pattern on the first two rows of the pocket chart using 14 or more square tiles (red, red, orange). Cover the 8th through the last square tile with Question Mark Cards. Follow the basic *Patterns* activity but instead of asking for the *next* color in the pattern sequence, point to the 12th pocket and ask students what color is under the Question Mark Card. Students hold up the square tile they think it is.

5–10 MIN CLASS

1 ACTIVITY

Introducing the Lunch Food Data Activity

Begin this activity by discussing what people usually eat for lunch.❶

People eat lots of different things for lunch, and lunch can have a lot of different parts to it. For example, sometimes my lunch is [a salad, yogurt, juice, and a cookie]. Sometimes it's [a sandwich, an apple, and milk]. What do you eat for lunch?

If your students all have the same school lunch, suggest that they think about what they eat for lunch at home or the meals that are served at school on different days. On the board or chart paper, list the foods that students name. They will refer to this list later in the session.

Today we are going to collect some information about the foods we eat for lunch. We will use this information to make a chart of our favorite lunch foods.

ACTIVITY

15–20 MIN INDIVIDUALS PAIRS

Generating Lunch Food Data

The first thing you will do is make a picture of everything you might eat and drink for lunch on one particular day. You can choose the day.

Distribute blank paper to each student. As needed, ask students questions to help them remember everything they usually eat for lunch.

Do you have something to drink? Do you have any fruits or vegetables? Do you have dessert?

Teaching Note

❶ **Using Children's Literature** Consider using children's literature to introduce the activity. Options include *This Is the Way We Eat Our Lunch: A Book About Children Around the World* by Edith Baer, *Lunch* by Denise Fleming, and *School Lunch* by True Kelley.

As the students work, remind them to think about all the different parts of their lunch.

Students draw pictures of the foods they eat for lunch.

When students have finished their drawings, organize the class into pairs or threes to share their lunch information with each other.

With your partner (or small group), take turns explaining the picture you drew. If you realize that you forgot to put something on your sheet, add it in.

After students have shared their drawings, the next task is to identify the favorite part of their lunch.

You had lots of delicious things in your lunches—it made me hungry! Now let's think about your very favorite part of lunch. Of all the things you drew on your paper—all of the different things you have for lunch—which one is your favorite?

Suggest that students tell their partners which is their favorite part of lunch.

I'm going to give each of you a card. Choose your favorite part of lunch and draw a picture of it on this card. Label your picture with a word that tells what is on your card.

Distribute an index card to each student. Point out that students should orient the cards horizontally to draw their favorite foods; having each piece of data the same shape helps when putting together the class data chart.

Sample Student Work

Professional Development

❷ **Teacher Note:** Sorting and Classifying, p. 129

❸ **Dialogue Box:** Is a Peach Dessert or Not?, p. 143

DISCUSSION

10–15 MIN CLASS

Sorting Favorite Lunch Food Data

Math Focus Points for Discussion

- Grouping data into categories based on similar attributes
- Sorting data in different ways
- Interpreting results of a data investigation

Gather students together with their completed cards showing favorite lunch foods. Begin by having students count off to determine the number of students present. Ask children to predict how many lunch cards there will be, and confirm this number by counting them.

Quickly go around the circle and ask each student to tell what food he or she drew on the card.

Are most of our favorite foods the same or different? Do our favorite foods have anything in common?

People chose different things. It might be easier to talk about our favorite foods if we put them into groups that have something in common. Do you see a way that some of these foods go together as a group?

List students' suggestions on chart paper or the board so that you can refer to their ideas later. Kindergarteners are likely to begin by grouping things that are exactly the same as they have, for example, a Pizza group, a Peanut Butter Sandwich group, a Macaroni and Cheese group, an Apple group, and a Potato Chip group. This approach usually results in a lot of categories with only a few items in each. Nevertheless, it is important for students to work on determining the categories for their lunch foods.❷

Some more general ways that kindergarteners have suggested categorizing their favorite foods are:

- healthy things/not healthy things (a mutually exclusive way of categorizing)
- desserts/drinks/sandwiches
- fruits/vegetables/things you drink/things with bread/cookies and cakes❸

If students are having a difficult time thinking of categories, make suggestions yourself.

Suppose one of our groups was Sweet Things. What foods do you think would go in this group? . . . What would go in the group that is Not Sweet Things? How could we make more groups out of the other foods that are Not Sweet Things? What could we call these other groups?

To help students see how the same set of data can be sorted in more than one way, plan to sort the lunch cards in several different ways. For the first sort, choose one set of categories from the list of student suggestions. For another sort, do a mutually exclusive set of two categories (e.g., Sweet Things and Not Sweet Things). At least one way of sorting should involve several categories.

To do sorting, students can either arrange their cards in groups in the middle of the circle, or they can take their cards and sit together in groups as a category is suggested.

Students sort their favorite lunch foods into categories.

When each sort is complete, ask students to comment on the results. Interpreting the data once they have been organized is an important part of working with data. You can encourage students to comment on the data with questions like these:

- How many people chose fruit as the favorite part of their lunch?
- Are there more people who chose brown foods as the favorite part of their lunch or more people who chose white foods as a favorite part of their lunch?

- Why do you think more people chose sweet foods as their favorite food than not sweet foods?
- Do you think if we asked the fourth graders about the favorite parts of their lunch, they would have the same favorite foods?

Encourage students, as necessary, with your own observations. You might, for example, note all the different kinds of fruit that people like, or express surprise that everyone did not list dessert as their favorite part of lunch.

When students have had the chance to sort the data in a few different ways and to discuss the results, either you or the class chooses one set of categories to use for a large class representation of the data.

You have a lot of good ideas for organizing the information about the favorite part of our lunches. Now we're going to choose one way to sort the foods and glue our cards down on paper so that we can save our representation. It seems that a lot of people were thinking about [desserts], so let's use the groups [Dessert and Not Dessert] in our representation.

Show students the large paper you have prepared for this lunch data chart. Write the categories at the bottom.

We are going to organize our lunch cards on this paper. I have written [Dessert and Not Dessert] at the bottom. Think about the food that is on your lunch card and decide which group it belongs in.

A few at a time, students place their cards in the section they chose. Have available glue sticks or tape. Encourage students to make columns by placing each card above the previous one in their category. There may be some discussion among students as to which category is the right one for certain foods. This is one of the important issues in working with categorical data. It is a good idea to let each student decide and explain the choice he or she made.

When the chart is finished, ask students to tell you about the representation. Record their observations on another sheet of chart paper. At the end of this session, find a place to post both the large data chart and the list of student observations.

SESSION FOLLOW-UP
4 Practice

Practice: For reinforcement of this unit's content, have students complete *Student Activity Book* page 76.

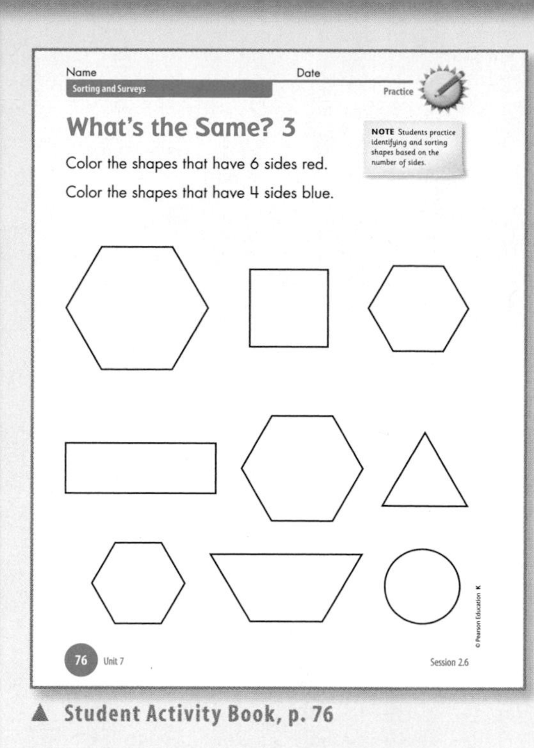
Name Date
Sorting and Surveys
Practice

What's the Same? 3

NOTE Students practice identifying and sorting shapes based on the number of sides.

Color the shapes that have 6 sides red.

Color the shapes that have 4 sides blue.

76 Unit 7 Session 2.6

© Pearson Education K

▲ **Student Activity Book, p. 76**

INVESTIGATION 3

Mathematical Emphases

Data Analysis Sorting and classifying

Math Focus Points

- Using attributes to sort a set of objects

Data Analysis Carrying out a data investigation

Math Focus Points

- Choosing a survey question with two possible responses
- Collecting and keeping track of survey data
- Interpreting results of a data investigation
- Using data to solve a problem

Data Analysis Representing data

Math Focus Points

- Making a representation of a set of data

Data Projects

Session	Student Activity Book	Student Math Handbook Flip Chart	Professional Development: Read Ahead of Time
SESSION 3.1 p. 100 **"Do You Like . . . ?" Surveys** Students develop their own "Do You Like . . . ?" survey questions to ask other students in the class. They then decide how they will record the responses to their questions.	77	45, 46	• **Teacher Note:** "Do You Like . . . ?" Survey Questions, p. 131
SESSION 3.2 p. 106 **Collecting Data** Students collect and record responses to their survey question. Math Workshop focuses on sorting objects by attribute and collecting data.	77	20, 45, 46, 47	• **Teacher Note:** Examining Students' Records of Survey Responses, p. 132 • **Dialogue Box:** Will All Our Seeds Germinate?, p. 144
SESSION 3.3 p. 111 **Sharing "Do You Like . . . ?" Surveys** Students finish collecting their survey data. They share the results of their surveys with the rest of the class.		20, 45, 46, 47	
SESSION 3.4 p. 114 **End-of-Unit Assessment: Solving a Problem Using Attendance Data** Students solve a problem using the attendance data from their classroom. Students determine who is absent, and then use this information along with the total number of students in the class to determine how many students are in school that day. They make a model or representation to explain how they determined the number of students in school.		45, 46	• **Teacher Note:** Assessing Students as They Use Data to Solve Problems, p.135
SESSION 3.5 p. 119 **End-of-Unit Assessment and How Did You Solve the Problem?** Students finish working on the assessment problem they began in the previous session. Math Workshop activities are available as students finish. The session ends with a class discussion in which students share how they used attendance data to figure out how many students were in school.	78		

Classroom Routines See page 16 for an overview.

Attendance

- No materials needed

Today's Question

- *Today's Question* chart for Session 3.2. See instructions on page 106.

Calendar

- Class calendar

Patterns on the Pocket Chart

- Pocket chart(s) or Sentence Pocket Chart
- M7, Question Mark Cards (from Investigation 1)
- M6, Arrow Cards (from Investigation 1)

Materials to Gather	Materials to Prepare
• **Chart paper**	• **Chart paper** Create a two-column chart titled "Do you like applesauce?" Title the two columns "Yes" and "No" at the top. • **Class list** Make copies. (1 per student)
• **Class list** (1 per student) See Session 3.1. • **Materials for the Counting Jar routine** (as you have set it up) • **Materials for Attribute Dominoes** See Session 2.5. • **Materials for Boxes, Bottles, and Cans** See Session 2.3.	• **Counting Jar** Place 24 familiar objects in the jar. (cubes, counters, etc.)
• **Materials for "Do you like. . . ?" Surveys** See Session 3.1. • **Materials for Counting Jar** See Session 3.2. • **Materials for Attribute Dominoes** See Session 2.5. • **Materials for Boxes, Bottles, and Cans** See Session 2.3. • **Students' completed recordings of their survey responses**	
• **Materials for creating data representations such as:** Connecting cubes, buttons, dot stickers, 1-inch squares of colored paper • **Drawing supplies** • **Glue sticks or tape** • **Completed and blank copies of Assessment Checklist** M3, M4, M8 ☑ • **Students' completed recordings of their survey responses**	
• **Materials for How Many Are Here Today?** See Session 3.4. • **Materials for Counting Jar** See Session 3.2. • **Materials for Attribute Dominoes** See Session 2.5. • **Students' completed recordings of their survey responses**	

☑ Checklist Available

"Do You Like . . . ?" Surveys

Math Focus Points

- Choosing a survey question with two possible responses
- Collecting and keeping track of survey data

Vocabulary

survey
data

Today's Plan		Materials
1 ACTIVITY **Introducing "Do You Like . . . ?" Surveys**	10–15 MIN CLASS	• *Student Activity Book,* p. 77 • Chart: "Do you like applesauce?"* ; class list*
2 ACTIVITY **Choosing a "Do You Like . . . ?" Survey Question**	10–15 MIN INDIVIDUALS PAIRS	• *Student Activity Book,* p. 77 • Class list
3 DISCUSSION **What's Your Question?**	10–15 MIN CLASS	• Chart paper
4 SESSION FOLLOW-UP **Practice**		• *Student Math Handbook Flip Chart,* pp. 45, 46

*See *Materials to Prepare,* p. 99.

Classroom Routines

Attendance: Counting Forward and Back Count around the circle as usual, and then have students count backward from the total number to one. Begin with the student who counted last so that each student says the same number but the count will be backward rather than forward. Encourage students to use the calendar or the number line to help them keep track of the numbers.

ACTIVITY

1 Introducing "Do You Like . . . ?" Surveys

Post the chart you prepared with the question "Do you like applesauce?" written on it. (See page 102.)❶ Read aloud the question.❷

Have students record their responses in whatever way they usually record them for *Today's Question.*

What do you notice about this survey?

This open-ended question gives students an opportunity to share their observations about the survey before looking at specific aspects of the data collected.

What do you notice about whether students in this class like applesauce or not?

Students might say:

"Ten people like applesauce, eight people don't like applesauce."

"More people like applesauce."

"It looks like it's about the same number of people."

Listen to students and encourage them to make observations that involve numbers and comparisons. If students do not comment on the specific number of people who answered yes or no, ask them to do so. Write these numbers next to the appropriate column on the chart.

How many people answered this survey? How could we figure that out?

Some students may suggest counting all the names. Others may know that the number should be equal to the number of students in school that day. Check the amount both ways.

Teaching Notes

❶ **Structuring Data Collection** During Sessions 3.2 and 3.3, students collect data by asking their own survey questions of other students in the class. This data collection is built into Math Workshop. Some teachers have used alternative structures for this activity. Some teachers choose to have all students do their surveys at the same time so that the activity is contained in the same class period and does not interrupt other students' work. Other teachers choose to have students collect their survey data at other times of the day, outside of math time. If you choose one of these alternative structures, you will need to adapt the suggested timetable and pacing for the next 2 sessions.

❷ **Choosing a Relevant "Do You Like . . . ?" Question** "Do you like applesauce?" is a question that is relevant in most classes because most students are familiar with applesauce. You can choose a different question that seems more relevant to your students to introduce "Do You Like . . . ?" surveys. You might choose something connected to your school (e.g., Do you like to play on the swings?) or an experience you know all students are familiar with (e.g., Do you like going to the beach?).

Professional Development

❸ **Teacher Note:** "Do You Like . . . ?" Survey Questions, p. 131

For the next few days, you will have a chance to do your own surveys. You are going to ask students in this class a question that you choose and collect their answers to your question. When you do your surveys, you will start with the question, Do You Like . . . ? You can finish that question however you want. For example, I asked you the question "Do you like *applesauce?*"

Do you like applesauce?	
Yes	No
Jae	Tammy
Beth	Mitchell
Victor	Russell
Kaitlyn	Abby
cindy	Lisa
Lionel	Mia
EMMA	Timothy
KYLE	Brad
DENNIS	
Jack	

Explain to students that the possible answers to their "Do you like . . . ?" questions should be either yes or no.

Ask students for their suggestions for "Do You Like . . . ?" questions and list these questions on chart paper or the board. If students come up with questions to which the responses would not be yes or no, help them think about how to reformulate their question. Encourage students to include on the list a variety of questions. For example, if students only come up with questions about food, help them to think about other subject areas such as what they like to do in their free time.❸

Then, introduce the tools students might use for collecting data: a class list, *Student Activity Book* page 77, or blank paper.

You can choose one of these papers to keep track of your classmates' answers to your question. This class list has everyone's name on it. How could you use this list to help you collect your survey data?

Students might say:

"You could put a circle next to people you ask."

"I could put blue next to Victor if he says yes and red if he says no."

Next, direct student attention to *Student Activity Book* page 77.

This one has a column that says yes and a column that says no. How could you use this chart to keep track of your data?

Some students may suggest putting check marks or other symbols under each column for each student's response. Others may suggest writing the names of the students under the response they give.

Finally, show students the blank piece of paper.

Or you can use a blank sheet of paper to keep track of everyone's answers. How might you keep track of your data on a piece of paper?

Students may have a variety of ideas for how to use the piece of paper for recording classmates' responses.

ACTIVITY 2

10–15 MIN INDIVIDUALS PAIRS

Choosing a "Do You Like . . . ?" Survey Question

Tell students that they are now going to spend some time deciding on a "Do You Like . . . ?" survey question to ask their classmates and choosing a method for recording students' responses. Students should choose from one of the three recording sheets you discussed. Ask the students to write the question they choose on their recording sheet and decide how they are going to use the sheet.

Name Date

Sorting and Surveys

"Do You Like . . . ?" Survey Chart

Do you like ______________?

YES	NO

Sessions 3.1, 3.2 Unit 7 77

▲ Student Activity Book, p. 77

Some students may want to work with a partner on this activity, though many will be so invested in their own question that they will want to work alone.

If students finish choosing their question and recording methods before you are ready to come back together, they should check in with you about their chosen methods to make sure both are reasonable. They can then begin collecting responses from their classmates. You may need to have a brief discussion with these students about how to approach the other students, who will be finishing up their own work, in order to ask their survey question in a way that will not disturb them too much.

ONGOING ASSESSMENT: Observing Students at Work

Students develop a survey question with two possible responses and decide how they will keep track of and record the survey data.

- **Can students come up with a "Do You Like . . . ?" survey question to which yes or no are the possible responses?**
- **Can students decide on a way to keep track of students' responses?** How do they choose to record responses? Does their recording method make sense?

DIFFERENTIATION: Supporting the Range of Learners

ELL Students might need help formulating their survey questions. English Language Learners might also need to practice saying their questions aloud so their classmates can easily understand them when they administer their surveys.

3 DISCUSSION

What's Your Question?

Math Focus Points for Discussion

- Choosing a survey question with two possible responses

Ask students to share the kind of "Do You Like . . . ?" question they chose as well as the specific question they chose. Record this information in a chart on chart paper.

Who chose a question about a kind of food? What question did you choose about food? Who chose a question about liking a game or an activity? What question did you choose? Who chose a question about a TV show or movie? What question did you choose? Did anyone ask another question? What question did you choose?

Do You Like . . . ? Survey Questions

Foods	Games/ Activities	TV Shows/ Movies	Other
pizza fruit cereal apples breakfast	swings tag reading		the ocean

Examine your list, and comment on what you notice about the data in the categories. Use numbers whenever possible when making these observations.

I see that 12 people chose survey questions about food, and a lot fewer, only 4, chose survey questions about animals.

4 SESSION FOLLOW-UP Practice

Student Math Handbook: Use the *Student Math Handbook Flip Chart* pages 45, 46 to reinforce content from today's session. See pages 146–148 in the back of this unit.

Collecting Data

Math Focus Points

- Collecting and keeping track of survey data
- Using attributes to sort a set of objects

Vocabulary

response

Today's Plan		Materials
MATH WORKSHOP 1 Collecting Data and Sorting 1A "Do You Like . . . ?" Surveys 1B Counting Jar 1C *Attribute Dominoes* 1D Boxes, Bottles, and Cans	20–35 MIN	1A • *Student Activity Book,* p. 77 • Class list (from Session 3.1) 1B • Counting Jar*; materials for the Counting Jar (as you have set it up) 1C • Materials from Session 2.5, p. 84 1D • Materials from Session 2.3, p. 75
DISCUSSION 2 Recording Responses	10 MIN CLASS	
SESSION FOLLOW-UP 3 Practice		• *Student Math Handbook Flip Chart,* pp. 20, 45, 46, 47

*See *Materials to Prepare,* p. 99.

Classroom Routines

Today's Question: Do you have the letter S in your name? On chart paper, create a horizontal table titled "Do you have the letter *S* in your name?" with the heading "Yes" written at the left of one row and "No" written at the left of the other row. Students respond by writing their names in the appropriate row. As you discuss the results of the survey, continue to have students experiment with different ways to organize the data so that it is easier to tell which group has more.

1 MATH WORKSHOP

Collecting Data and Sorting

20–35 MIN

Explain that the following four activities are available during this Math Workshop. Remind students what each activity entails, what materials are required, and where they are located.

Briefly discuss how students who are conducting their surveys should approach the other students to ask their question in a way that will disturb them the least as they do their own work.

1A "Do You Like . . . ?" Surveys

INDIVIDUALS PAIRS

Students collect and record responses to their surveys. ❶ ❷ ❸

Students collect survey data.

ONGOING ASSESSMENT: Observing Students at Work

Students collect and record data.

- **How do students record the responses to their survey?** Do they use the class list? The survey chart? Do they write each student's name? Record with check marks?
- **Do students have a system for keeping track of who they have surveyed so far?**
- **What do students do when they get an answer that is not *yes* or *no* (e.g., maybe, don't know)?** Do they make another category or ignore the response?

Teaching Notes

❶ **Assembling a Portfolio** Students choose a survey question and collect and record the data in response to that question. Collect students' records of their classmate's responses. This will give you information about how students recorded and kept track of a set of data.

❷ **Collecting Data from Only Some Students** Most kindergarteners are engaged first and foremost by the process of collecting data, which can be a good socially engaging event. Issues such as collecting data from everyone in the class may not seem important to them or may not even occur to them. As this is the first experience students have with asking a survey question themselves, the emphasis is on engaging them in the process and not on making sure that students collect data from everyone in the class. Later, in the first grade data unit, students focus on ways to make sure they have asked everyone a survey question.

❸ **Maybe, I Don't Know, I Can't Decide** Students may encounter responses to their survey that do not fit neatly into *yes* or *no* categories. Figuring out how to deal with unexpected responses is a part of the data collection process. You may find that students simply ignore the response, put it in either the *yes* or *no* category, or decide to create a new category. If students come to you with this problem, help them think through what they can do with the response. You will discuss this issue in the discussion at the end of the session.

DIFFERENTIATION: Supporting the Range of Learners

Intervention If some students are not recording the responses to their survey and seem unsure of how to do so, suggest a particular method you think will work well for them. Using a class list is particularly helpful for students who have difficulty writing.

1B Counting Jar

INDIVIDUALS

Students count the objects in the Counting Jar (24 objects students are familiar with, such as cubes, counters, etc.). They make a set of the same size, and then find a way to record what they found out.

ONGOING ASSESSMENT: Observing Students at Work

Students count a set of objects, create an equivalent set, and record their work.

- **How do students count the objects in the jar?** Do they organize the objects in any way? Do they know the sequence of number names? Do they count each item once and only once? Do they double-check?
- **Do they easily count 24 objects?** Is there a number at which they have difficulty? Do they come up with different numbers if they count more than once? If they are able to count up to 24, can they also create a set of 24 objects?
- **How do students create an equivalent set?** Do they think, "The Counting Jar had 24. I need 24 tiles. 1, 2, 3, . . ."? Do they recreate the Counting Jar set, matching the items 1 to 1? Do they double-check?
- **How do students record their work?** Do they draw a picture of the items? Write numbers? Both?

1C *Attribute Dominoes*

PAIRS

For complete details about this activity, see Session 2.5, page 85.

DIFFERENTIATION: Supporting the Range of Learners

Extension Students can adapt the rules of this game so that blocks can only be placed next to each other if they have *only* one attribute the same or *exactly* two attributes the same.

1D Boxes, Bottles, and Cans

For complete details about this activity, see Session 2.3, page 76.

10 MIN CLASS

DISCUSSION

2 Recording Responses

Math Focus Points for Discussion

- Collecting and keeping track of survey data

Students who have already asked their survey questions should bring the sheets on which they recorded responses to this discussion.

Ask students to share how they are recording or plan to record other students' responses. Compare a few different methods.

Once you record your responses, you want to be able to look at your sheet and get some information from it. Let's look at [Beth's] sheet. [Beth] used the class list and wrote yes or no next to each person's name. [Jae] made up [his] own sheet. [Jae] made a green circle for each person who liked pizza and a red circle for each person who didn't. How are their sheets different? . . . What can you find out from [Beth's] sheet? What can you find out from [Jae's] sheet?

Ask students to talk about what they notice about a few different ways of recording and the information they can get from each way.

Next, address the issue of how to record students' responses that are not yes or no.

I notice that some of you got responses to your survey that were not yes or no. A few people answered "maybe" or "I don't know" or "I can't choose." How did you record those responses?

Students might say:

"I wrote 'maybe' and I wrote [Jason's] name and [Mary's] name."

"I just didn't record those. I didn't write down [Sarah] because she couldn't choose."

Professional Development

④ **Teacher Note:** Examining Students' Records of Survey Responses, p. 132

⑤ **Dialogue Box:** Will All Our Seeds Germinate?, p. 144

Ask students to think about what they plan to do if they get a response that is not yes or no.④ ⑤

Once they have collected their responses, end by asking the class to count how many students gave each response and record the amounts on their recording sheet. Discuss briefly how they might record the amounts on each of the different kinds of recording sheets.

3

SESSION FOLLOW-UP

Practice

Student Math Handbook Flip Chart: Use the *Student Math Handbook Flip Chart* pages 20, 45, 46, 47 to reinforce content from today's session. See pages 146–148 in the back of this unit.

Sharing "Do You Like . . . ?" Surveys

Math Focus Points

- Collecting and keeping track of survey data
- Interpreting results of a data investigation

Today's Plan		Materials
1 MATH WORKSHOP **Collecting Data and Sorting** 1A "Do You Like . . . ?" Surveys 1B Counting Jar 1C *Attribute Dominoes* 1D Boxes, Bottles, and Cans	20–30 MIN	1A • Materials from Session 3.2, p. 106 1B • Materials from Session 3.2, p. 106 1C • Materials from Session 2.5, p. 84 1D • Materials from Session 2.3, p. 75
2 DISCUSSION **Sharing "Do You Like . . . ?" Surveys**	10–15 MIN CLASS	• Students' completed recordings of their survey responses
3 SESSION FOLLOW-UP **Practice**		• *Student Math Handbook Flip Chart,* pp. 20, 45, 46, 47

Classroom Routines

Calendar: How Many Days . . . ? Students use the calendar to determine how many days have passed since a class event or holiday that happened this month, or for a challenge, an event that occurred last month. Discuss students' strategies for determining the number of days.

MATH WORKSHOP

1 Collecting Data and Sorting

Explain that the following four activities are available during this Math Workshop and that today is the last day Boxes, Bottles, and Cans will be available. Students also need to finish their surveys by the end of this session.

1A "Do You Like . . . ?" Surveys

For complete details about this activity, see Session 3.2, page 107.

DIFFERENTIATION: Supporting the Range of Learners

Extension Students who are interested can do another survey. They can choose a different "Do you like . . . ?" question or another type of question.

1B Counting Jar

For complete details about this activity, see Session 3.2, page 108.

1C *Attribute Dominoes*

For complete details about this activity, see Session 2.5, page 85.

1D Boxes, Bottles, and Cans

For complete details about this activity, see Session 2.3, page 76.

DISCUSSION

10–15 MIN CLASS

2 Sharing "Do You Like . . . ?" Surveys

Math Focus Points for Discussion

- Interpreting results to a data investigation

Gather students together to discuss their completed surveys. Students should bring their recording sheets with them.

Ask each student to briefly share the results of his or her survey by answering the following questions:

- What did you ask?
- What did you find out?
- How many people said yes and how many said no? How many people responded with a different answer?

Model for students how to share the results to their survey by sharing the results to the initial survey you did with the whole class:

I did a survey about whether or not people like applesauce and I found out that more people in our class do like applesauce but not a lot more. Ten people do like applesauce, eight people don't like applesauce, and one person has never eaten it.

Have as many students share as time allows. Students who did not share their survey results today can do so during the next session.

DIFFERENTIATION: Supporting the Range of Learners

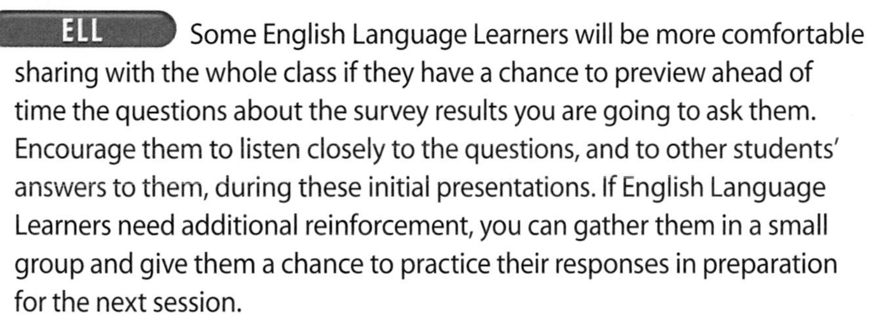

ELL Some English Language Learners will be more comfortable sharing with the whole class if they have a chance to preview ahead of time the questions about the survey results you are going to ask them. Encourage them to listen closely to the questions, and to other students' answers to them, during these initial presentations. If English Language Learners need additional reinforcement, you can gather them in a small group and give them a chance to practice their responses in preparation for the next session.

3 SESSION FOLLOW-UP
Practice

Student Math Handbook Flip Chart: Use the *Student Math Handbook Flip Chart* pages 20, 45, 46, 47 to reinforce content from today's session. See pages 146–148 in the back of this unit.

Teaching Note

1 Preparing for the End-of-Unit Assessment Before Session 3.4, gather the assessment checklists you have filled in over the course of this unit—Assessment Checklist: Representations of Data (M3), Assessment Checklist: Using Data to Solve Problems (M4), and Assessment Checklist: Sorting (M8). For each benchmark, look over your notes, and sort students into three categories: those who have clearly met the benchmark, those who have not yet met the benchmark, and those you have questions about. You will need to focus your observations on the students in the latter two categories over the course of Sessions 3.4 and 3.5. Make a list of students you need to observe for each benchmark.

End-of-Unit Assessment: Solving a Problem Using Attendance Data

Math Focus Points

- Making a representation of a set of data
- Using data to solve a problem
- Interpreting results of a data investigation

Today's Plan			Materials
ACTIVITY 1 **Introducing the Problem**	10–15 MIN	CLASS	• Materials for creating data representations such as connecting cubes, buttons, dot stickers, 1-inch squares of colored paper; drawing supplies; glue sticks or tape; 12″ x 8″ paper
ACTIVITY 2 **How Many Are Here Today?**	15–25 MIN	INDIVIDUALS	• M4 ✓ * • Materials from Activity 1
DISCUSSION 3 **Sharing "Do You Like . . . ?" Surveys,** *continued*	10 MIN	CLASS	• Student's completed recording of their survey responses
SESSION FOLLOW-UP 4 **Practice**			• *Student Math Handbook Flip Chart,* pp. 45, 46

*See *Materials to Prepare,* p. 99.

Classroom Routines

Patterns on the Pocket Chart: What Comes Here? Arrange an ABCD repeating pattern on the first two rows of the pocket chart using 14 or more arrow cards (up, left, down, right). Cover the eighth through the last Arrow Card with Question Mark Cards. Follow the basic *Patterns* activity, but instead of asking for the *next* direction in the pattern sequence, point to the 12th pocket and ask students what direction is under the Question Mark Card. Students point in the direction they think it is.

10–15 MIN CLASS

ACTIVITY 1 Introducing the Problem

In this session, the daily attendance routine is used as the basis for using data to solve a problem. Because this problem involves counting and representing information, you can use it to assess how students represent data (Benchmark 1) and how they work with data to solve a problem (Benchmark 2).❶

Today we're going to think about attendance as a mathematical problem. Let's start with the number of people in our class. When everyone is here, how many of us are in the room?

Students can decide whether to limit the count to themselves or to include adults present in the classroom. This number should be very familiar to the students. Write this number on the board or chart paper.

Ask students to help you name their classmates who are not in school today. List these names on the board or chart paper as well. Do not count or figure out how many people are in class today. This is the problem students will work on.

Here is the math problem I would like you to think about. We know that when everyone is in school there are [25] students in our class. Today [four] students are not here. The problem is this. How many students are here in class today? Your job is to figure out this problem. You can use some of these materials to help you.

Show students the materials you have available for solving the problem. Explain to them that when they are finished solving the problem, they also need to figure out a way to show their work on paper.

Some students may be eager to share their ideas for solving this problem. Since you are trying to get a sense of how each student will approach this task, explain to the class that you will talk about the problem and their ideas for solving it once everyone has had a chance to work on it.

Students may wonder why you are not just counting everyone who is in class today as you do on other days. Acknowledge this, and tell students that you are also interested in other ways of figuring out how many people are in the room.

One way to solve this problem is to count everyone like we do when we take attendance. There are also other ways to use the information you have to solve the problem.❷

Teaching Note

❶ **What if no one is absent?** Because this problem relies on some students being absent, you will need to plan for what to do if in fact everyone is present. You can consider saving the problem for another day, or you can create a new problem using attendance data from a previous session when students were absent.

Math Note

❷ **Working with a Quantity Above 20** If there are more than 20 students in your class, students will be working with a quantity above 20 as they solve this problem. Because they are so familiar with the context of taking attendance, and the number of students in their class is a meaningful amount to them, they may be quite comfortable with this number. However, this does not necessarily mean that students can work as successfully with these same quantities as with those in other problems.

Professional Development

④ **Teacher Notes:** Kindergarteners' Representations of Data, p. 123; Assessing Students as They Use Data to Solve Problems, p. 135

Teaching Note

⑤ **Recording Solutions Using Models** Note that many students solve the problem by creating a model that involves some action—for example, building a tower of 25 cubes and taking away four. Actions are sometimes difficult for students to represent. Work with these students to think about how they might show this solution on paper.

ACTIVITY

How Many Are Here Today?

15–25 MIN INDIVIDUALS

Students work individually on this problem. As students finish their models, pictures, or drawings, suggest that they write a title.

By the end of this unit, students are expected to be able to represent a set of data (Benchmark 1) and use data to solve problems (Benchmark 2). This means that they identify data to use to solve a problem, accurately solve the problem, and explain or show how they solved the problem. Use Assessment Checklists: Representations of Data (M3) and Using Data to Solve Problems (M4) to keep track of your observations as students solve this problem.④ ⑤

Assessment Checklist: Using Data to Solve Problems

Student	Identifies and represents data needed to solve the problem	Solves the problem accurately	Representation shows how the student solved the problem	Notes
Kiyo	✓	✓	no, explained but didn't know how to show	22 cubes took 4 away, counted
Lisa	counted # of kids here today	✓	✓	drew 18 people numbered
Laquinta	no, drew only 20 dots	no, 16	✓	counting ?? crossed out 4 but started w/ 20
Brad	✓ put out 22 buttons + 4 buttons for absent	no		didn't know how to use info
Tammy	✓	✓	✓	wrote 1, 2, 3 etc. to 22 crossed out 4

ONGOING ASSESSMENT: Observing Students at Work

Students use data about the class to figure out how many students are present. They represent how they solved the problem.

- **Do students understand that the problem involves several pieces of information: the total number of students in the class, the number of students absent, and the number of students present?** Do they know that they are trying to figure out how many students are present?
- **What strategies do students use to solve the problem?** Do they build a model with cubes or counters? Do they use the total number of people in the class and the number absent to help them? Do students use counting strategies, such as counting up from the number of absent students to the total number, or counting back from the total number of students in the class? Do they distribute a counter to each student present and then collect those counters and count to determine how many people are present?
- **Are students able to explain their strategy for solving the problem?** Is their strategy apparent from their representation?

DIFFERENTIATION: Supporting the Range of Learners

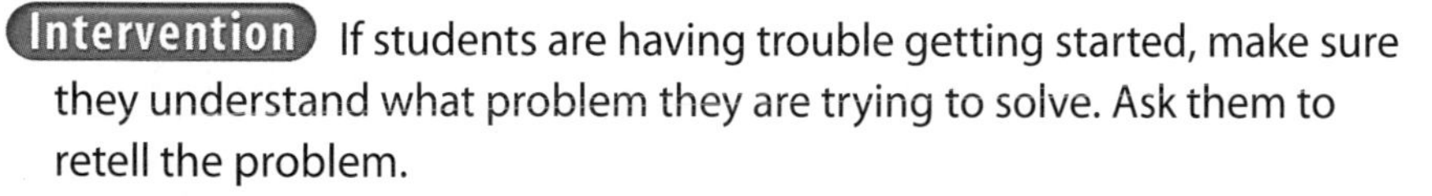

Intervention If students are having trouble getting started, make sure they understand what problem they are trying to solve. Ask them to retell the problem.

Intervention If students are unsure how to solve the problem, help them break it into parts. You might ask questions such as:

How many students are in our class? How could you show that? How many of those students are absent today? How could you show that? So then how many people are here today?

Intervention If students have used a strategy to solve the problem but do not know how to show how they solved it, ask them to explain what they did and work together as a class to come up with a representation of their strategy.

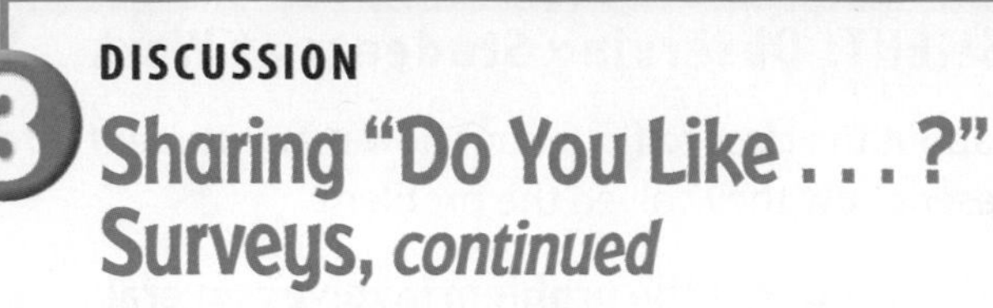

3 DISCUSSION
Sharing "Do You Like . . . ?" Surveys, *continued*

Math Focus Points for Discussion

◆ Interpreting results of a data investigation

Students who did not share their survey results during the last session do so today. Ask each student who shares some of the same questions:

- What did you ask and what did you find out?
- How many people said yes and how many said no?
- Did anyone say anything different than yes or no? What did you do about that?

If time permits, end the discussion by asking students to talk about the experience of doing surveys.

For most of you, this was the first time you did a survey on your own. It was hard work to record your data and to think about what you found. What advice do you have for each other about how to do surveys? What would you do differently next time?

Assure students that they will have many opportunities in first and second grade, as well as later in their lives, to do surveys. Tell them that they will learn more about how to ask questions, collect data, organize data, and figure out what the data means each time.

4 SESSION FOLLOW-UP
Practice

Student Math Handbook Flip Chart: Use the *Student Math Handbook Flip Chart* pages 45, 46 to reinforce content from today's session. See pages 146–148 in the back of this unit.

End-of-Unit Assessment and How Did You Solve the Problem?

Math Focus Points

- Making a representation of a set of data
- Using data to solve a problem

Today's Plan		Materials
1 MATH WORKSHOP **Counting Students** 1A How Many Are Here Today? 1B Counting Jar 1C *Attribute Dominoes*	20–35 MIN	1A • Materials from Session 3.4, p. 114 1B • Materials from Session 3.2, p. 106 1C • Materials from Session 2.5, p. 84
2 DISCUSSION **How Did You Solve the Problem?**	10 MIN CLASS	• Students' representations of their solutions to the problem
3 SESSION FOLLOW-UP **Practice**		• *Student Activity Book,* p. 78

Classroom Routines

Attendance: Counting Forward and Back Count around the circle as usual, and then have students count backward from the total number to one. Begin with the student who counted last so that each student will say the same number, but the count will be backward rather than forward. Encourage students to use the calendar or the number line to help them keep track of the numbers.

Teaching Note

➊ **Benchmark 3** Observe any students who have not yet met Benchmark 3 (sort a set of objects according to their attributes) while they play *Attribute Dominoes*, or play a round with them.

Professional Development

➋ **Teacher Note:** Sorting and Classifying, p. 129

➌ **Teacher Note:** Assessing Students as They Use Data to Solve Problems, p. 135

MATH WORKSHOP

Counting Students

20–35 MIN

Explain that the following three activities are available during this Math Workshop. Students who have not yet finished working on the "How Many Are Here Today?" problem should finish their work during this time.

1A How Many Are Here Today?

INDIVIDUALS

Students continue to work on solving and recording their strategies for the "How Many Are Here Today?" problem. Tell students they will continue to use the data from yesterday, not today even if more or fewer students are absent today.

For complete details about this activity, see Session 3.4, page 115.

1B Counting Jar

INDIVIDUALS

For complete details about this activity, see Session 3.2, page 108.

1C *Attribute Dominoes*

PAIRS

For complete details about this activity, see Session 2.5, page 85.➊➋

DISCUSSION

2 How Did You Solve the Problem?

10 MIN CLASS

Math Focus Points for Discussion

- Using data to solve a problem

Ask students to bring their representations of how they solved the problem with them to the discussion, or gather students where they can see everyone's work.

Ask a few volunteers to show and explain their ways of solving the problem. As each student shares, ask others to raise their hand if they used the same material or solved the problem in a similar way. This will acknowledge each student's work without taking the time for everyone to share individually.➌

In order to show the range of possibilities, call on students who used different materials to represent the data or different methods to solve the problem.

Jason's Work

Lisa's Work

SESSION FOLLOW-UP

3 Practice

Practice: For enrichment of this unit's content, have students complete *Student Activity Book* page 78.

Name Date

Sorting and Surveys — Practice

Favorite Meals

NOTE Students analyze survey data and conduct a survey to collect data.

Beth asks her friends, "Which meal do you like best?" She marks their answers on the chart.

Breakfast	Lunch	Dinner
4 stick figures	10 stick figures	6 stick figures

1. How many people like breakfast best? ________
2. Which meal do most people like best? ________
3. How many people did Beth ask? ________
4. Ask some friends which meal they like best. Record your data. ________

Breakfast	Lunch	Dinner

78 Unit 7 Session 3.4

▲ Student Activity Book, p. 78

Professional Development

UNIT 7

Sorting and Surveys

Teacher Notes

In Part 6 of *Implementing Investigations in Kindergarten,* you will find a set of Teacher Notes that addresses topics and issues applicable to the curriculum as a whole rather than to specific curriculum units. They include the following:

Computational Fluency and Place Value

Computational Algorithms and Methods

Representations and Contexts for Mathematical Work

Foundations of Algebra in the Elementary Grades

Discussing Mathematical Ideas

Racial and Linguistic Diversity in the Classroom: What Does Equity Mean in Today's Math Classroom?

Dialogue Boxes

Kindergarteners' Representations of Data

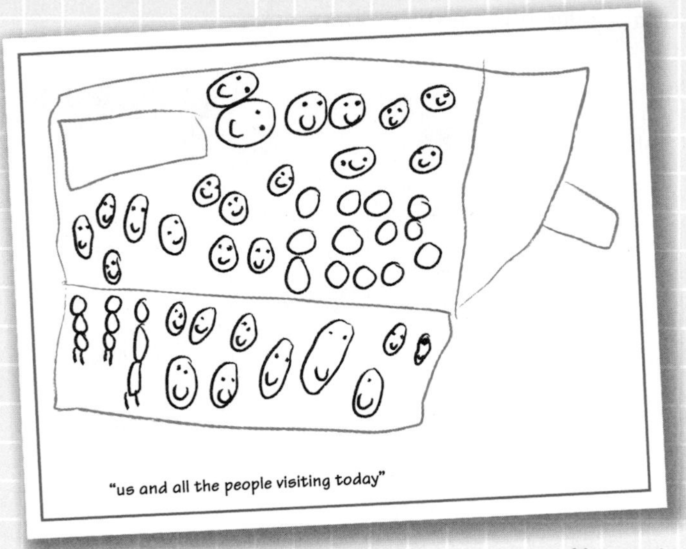

Abby's Work

A representation of data is both a way for students to keep track of their data and a way to communicate the results of data collection and analysis. There are many standard forms of data representation, including charts, tallies, line plots, and bar graphs. There are also many less standard and less familiar forms of graphs and diagrams that have been invented—and are still being invented—by statisticians and others to represent particular kinds of data sets. A good representation is not only a means of communication but also is a tool for better understanding the data.

In the primary grades, students' first uses of data representations should reflect the same central goal: to find ways of showing the data that help both the students themselves and others better "see" what the data show. When students are encouraged to invent their own ways of representing their data, they often come up with wonderfully individual pictures or unconventional graphs that help them communicate the meaning of the data.

This unit emphasizes the use of concrete materials and pictures to represent data that students collect. During the first investigation, students make representations that show the number of people in their classroom. Many kindergarteners will use objects such as counters or cube towers to represent the data, while others will show this information in a pictorial way. To represent similar data in Counting Noses, Counting Eyes, students are asked to use cubes to represent the number of noses in their class and then to put together a collection of pictures to represent the number of eyes.

In the second investigation, students show their favorite part of lunch by drawing pictures of each piece of data. Then, working together as a whole class, they explore different ways to organize these data and put them together in a large representation that will somewhat resemble a pictorial bar graph.

Students' representations will not necessarily follow the conventions of graphing that adults use. Often the pictures vary in size and are not lined up evenly, making it difficult to count them quickly and to compare the sizes of different groups. Students' early attempts at representing data do, however, convey information in a way that is meaningful to them and often to others, as well.

Consider the following range of representations students in one Kindergarten class made when asked to represent the number of students in their class.

A number of students attempted a drawing that included every person in the class. Two students succeeded in including everyone, while the others seemed to either lose track of the people in their representation or lose interest in drawing 23 figures. All of those students, however, were able to explain, "This is a drawing of the people in our class."

Kyle's Work

Other students used objects to represent the people in the class. A lot of them stacked connecting cubes into a tower, while others used counters to show the 23 students. This was a challenging task for some students.

Lisa uses cubes to represent the number of students in her class.

The students who used cubes or counters were more accurate in representing 23 than the students who made drawings. This was perhaps because the counters were easier to keep track of and required less effort than drawing 23 figures.

While most students used either drawings or counters, there were other interesting approaches as well. One student made a list of everyone in the class by consulting the photographs of each student that were posted on the door of the classroom. Another wrote the numbers 1 through 23 to show the people in the class, and two others used dot stickers to represent each person.

Cindy's Work

Encourage students to find their own ways to show data throughout this unit. When students are pushed to adopt conventions of what graphs are "supposed to" look like, too often they produce graphs that, for them, do not communicate anything about their data. By inventing and constructing their own representations, students will become more familiar with their data and remain clear about what their pictures or graphs represent.

One-to-One and Two-to-One Correspondence

One-to-One Correspondence

It is obvious to us as adults that if we put out a button for each student on the class list and there are 25 students, there will be 25 buttons. However, this correlation is not always obvious to five- and six-year-olds. In the class activity, How Many Are We?, students are developing some very basic ideas about how a model, be it a set of pictures or a set of buttons, can represent another set of things, such as all of the people in a class.

When one class worked on this activity, one student carefully placed a button on top of each name on the class list and then rearranged the buttons in a long line across the table. He counted the buttons several times until he was finally satisfied that there were 25.

Teacher: What did you do with the buttons?

Ricardo: I put a button in line for every name, and then I counted them and there were 25. But when I counted again, there were only 23, so I counted them again. See, 1, 2, 3, 4, . . . 23, 24, 25!

Teacher: And what do those buttons tell you?

Ricardo: That there are 25 students in the class. There is one for every student in the class.

Teacher: How do you know?

Ricardo: Because I put one in for each name, and there are 25 names and 25 kids in our class, and so there's 25 buttons.

Teacher: How do you know there are 25 names and buttons and students?

Ricardo: Because we've been counting the kids all year and there's 25 in our class, and the class list has everyone's name, and I put out one button for every name, and there's one name and one button for every kid.

Ricardo's understanding of the correspondence of names to buttons to people is apparent from the way he relates what he knows about the number of students in his class to the names on the class list and to the buttons he placed on all of the names. He expected there to be 25 buttons when he counted them. The fact that he miscounted the buttons but knew to count them again suggests that he understands one-to-one correspondence and the way counting gives information about the number of things in a group.

Another student used a similar approach to Ricardo's, placing one shell on each name on the class list.

Teacher: What did you use to show all of the students in the class?

Jennifer: Shells.

Teacher: And what do the shells tell you?

Jennifer: Um, I put one on everyone's name. And then I counted.

Teacher: I wonder . . . how many shells do you have?

Jennifer [shrugging her shoulders] I forget.

Teacher: Is there a way you could figure that out?

Jennifer: Uh-huh. Count them. See, 1, 2, 3, 4, 5 . . . . [She counts all of the shells, but occasionally loses track and arrives at 28.] No, I think that's too much.

Teacher: Too much what?

Jennifer: Too many shells. Last time I think I got 23 or 24.

Teacher: Could we count them together? You move each shell as we count so we'll know what we've already counted.

The teacher helps Jennifer recount the shells. This time Jennifer carefully touches each shell and slides it to one side as she counts.

Jennifer: 1, 2, 3, . . . [This time she accurately counts 25 shells.]

Teacher: So, what does that tell us?

Jennifer: That there are 25 shells?

Teacher: Does it help you know how many people there are?

Jennifer: Um, 25? But I could count the names and really find out.

In this exchange, Jennifer is beginning to make sense of how a model can represent other things. While she seems to have a sense of the rote-counting sequence, her ability to keep track of larger numbers is still a bit shaky. However, her comment that 28 seemed like too much suggests that she has a sense of what the number should be. By offering to recount together and suggesting moving the shells to keep track, the teacher gently supported Jennifer's counting strategies without being intrusive.

Two-to-One Correspondence

The relationships of *half* and *double* are key mathematical ideas. The two-to-one correspondence that students have noticed on their own bodies (with eyes, ears, hands, and so on), as well as in sharing activities ("two for you, two for me"), will lead them to critical ideas about multiplication, division, and ratios. Forming pairs and counting by 2s is also connected to later work in place value, when students discover that a group of things can be counted as one group and, at the same time, retain the value of the number of items in it (one group of ten and ten ones, for example).

Counting by groups of 2 is a challenging task for most kindergarteners. In fact, the concept will not be firmly understood by most students until second grade. Just as young students learn to chant the names of the numbers from 1 to 10 long before they can accurately count objects and have an understanding of quantity, they learn the counting-by-2s chant "2, 4, 6, 8" without understanding how it relates to counting. In fact, most young students cannot go beyond 8, and they often relate that sequence of numbers to the familiar chant "2, 4, 6, 8. Who do we appreciate?" rather than to sets of two objects.

Kindergarteners and first graders will begin to understand the two-to-one relationship as they identify things that come in 2s and talk about quantities as being *twice as much* or *double the amount.* Listen for remarks like these, which indicate students' growing understanding:

"We have twice as many eyes as noses."

"If you only counted one eye for everyone, that would be like noses. But eyes are double."

"You have to add 25 two times because you have two eyes for each person."

In Kindergarten, the major emphasis in counting should be on developing sound and effective strategies for counting by 1s. You can, however, model situations so that students begin to see concrete ways of representing pairs. For example, when students are using the class eye chart to count the total number of eyes, they see two eyes on each card, but they are still counting by 1s. The rhythm of the counting sequence can be used to point out something special about this count. As you point to each eye and count, you can emphasize every second number: "One, *two,* three, *four,* five, *six* . . ."

To emphasize the two-to-one correspondence of eyes to people, students could take two connecting cubes, one color for their right eye and another color for their left. Make a tower of right-eye cubes and a tower of left-eye cubes. Then, attach the two towers side by side so that students can see them as one set of data. These towers can then be compared to the cube "tower of noses," with students noting that now there are twice as many towers (and cubes) and twice as many eyes. Repeated experiences with models and opportunities to count by groups of two will reinforce students' understanding of two-to-one correspondence.

Dealing with Sensitive Issues

Some sensitive issues may arise when students are participating in such activities as Counting Noses and Counting Eyes. Students who wear glasses may be uncomfortable with the focus on eyes in the classroom. Some students may feel a little uncomfortable talking about body parts, and other students may name body parts that you think are not appropriate for the classroom. You will have to handle these remarks according to your own and your school's approach. In field-test classes, students were so engaged in the mathematics of the activity that the discussion of private body parts never arose. However, you might want to consider in advance how to keep the focus on the mathematics.

Another issue may arise in classrooms with a student who does not have the usual number of body parts (for example, a student who is missing an arm). If this is the case in your classroom, you will have already talked with your class about the student's special needs so that some matter-of-factness toward the student's differences will have been established.

Any differences should be included in the discussion as a mathematical issue. For example, you might say, "If we are going to count arms and Jason has one arm, how can we make sure we get the right count?" Depending on your own style and the atmosphere in the class, you can even make this a highlight of the mathematics: "We know we have 50 eyes, but Raul thinks something different will happen if we count arms. Who can predict how many arms we will have?" Such discussions are often much more uncomfortable for adults than for students, including the student who is different. That student is likely to be genuinely interested in such a problem.

Other sensitive issues may arise in counting eyes at home. Students who split their time between two parents or live with another relative may wonder which "home" they should count. They may also wonder whether to simply count family members or other people who may be living at home. For this activity, we are purposely leaving it up to students to establish which people they want to count in which home(s). Respect students' decisions about this, and focus the discussion on the counts of the eye cards that are brought in, rather than on whether everyone who "belongs" has been counted. Encourage students to count only humans who live in their homes. While some students may want to include pets, we suggest that you gently but firmly limit the data collection to people so that everyone feels included—including the students who have no pets.

Sorting and Classifying

Sorting and classifying is a central scientific, mathematical, and human activity. Important issues of classification arise in many disciplines: How can we classify library books in a systematic and useful way? Is this animal a new species or is it part of a class of animals that has already been identified and described? As students learn about their world, community, language, and culture, they are developing and organizing categories of information. For example, which foods are fruits? Which animals are dogs? Which behaviors are accepted at my house, at grandma's house, or in the park? For which words can you add *-ed* to indicate past tense?

In mathematics as in other areas, classification is an important activity. Shapes are classified by particular attributes such as number of sides or faces and types of angles. For example, a triangle is a polygon with three sides. Numbers are classified by particular characteristics as well. For example, a prime number is a number with exactly two factors, one and the number itself. Classifications must often be developed for collecting data. For example, for a rating scale of 1–5, how are "1" and "5" defined?

In the broadest sense, classification is about how things (people, animals, numbers, shapes, attitudes) are alike or different. Sorting any collection into categories requires attending to certain attributes and ignoring others. It is this skill of focusing on particular attributes to the exclusion of others that primary grade students are learning. For example, in order to identify a shape as a triangle, we attend only to certain characteristics—the number of sides and angles, the fact that each side is a line segment, and that the shape is closed (there are no breaks or gaps). We do not pay attention to the size, color, texture, or orientation of the shape in order to identify it as a triangle. While what to pay attention to and what to ignore may seem obvious to adults in this instance, the whole idea of classifying by particular attributes is an important new area for young students. They are beginning to learn how to look only at a particular attribute and ignore the rest, rather than look at the overall combination of attributes.

As kindergarteners sort a variety of sets, they describe and define their categories. In their work with surveys in this unit, students work with data that fit clearly into two defined categories (*yes* and *no*). When students respond to *Today's Question,* they are asked to reply within one of two categories. However, when they respond to their classmates' "Do You Like . . . ?" surveys, there are no restrictions on their responses, such that some questions of classification are likely to arise. Even though students start out with a survey question involving two choices, all responses may not fit neatly into the two categories. What if a student says, "I don't know" or "I can't decide" in response to a question such as "Do you like the ocean?" Such responses raise important issues about creating categories in data collection. Help students decide what they can do to reflect these data in their representations. Students might be tempted to simply ignore these data. Remind students that these responses are part of the information they are finding out. How can they keep track of these responses, and how can they represent them?

In their work with sorting sets of objects and sorting favorite lunch food data, students make decisions about how to define and name their categories. They must decide by what attributes to group objects or data and then decide in what category each object or piece of data fits. This is particularly challenging with more subjective attributes, such as size: Which boxes are small? Which are not small? Different students may have different ideas. Similar dilemmas arise when students are categorizing their favorite parts of their lunches. For example, how can the different foods be grouped? Sweet/Not Sweet? Vegetable/Fruit/Bread/Dessert? Does a peach go in the dessert category or the fruit category? What about foods that do not seem to fit into any of the categories?

Many students begin sorting by deciding upon one category that is important to them and finding everything that belongs in that category. For example, if a student's favorite lunch food is cookies, she might use Cookies as her starting place and find all of the other Cookie data. Implicitly, this student is sorting into Cookies and Not Cookies, which are two mutually exclusive categories. When students find all of the items that are the "same" as their own item (and also have a pile of items that are "different"), they are again sorting into two mutually exclusive groups. The important logical principle underlying this type of sorting is that a piece of data cannot belong in both groups. Of course, students often begin to realize that there could be a third category, such as "not sure," or "do not know" to account for data that do not clearly belong in one category or the other. This realization is important, because it means that students recognize that a good sorting scheme must account for all of the data—not just some pieces of data.

Kindergarteners also begin using more complex categorization strategies to sort information. Their sorting strategies for dealing with complex data sets often have flaws but lead to important realizations. For example, a student may start working with "portraits" by making a pile of everyone wearing red, then use the remaining cards to find people who have brown hair, and then switch again to find those who wear glasses. Adults understand that the categories "red clothes," "brown hair," and "glasses" involve different characteristics, and that they should instead be parallel (e.g., brown, blond, red, and black hair). While five- and six-year-olds cannot always maintain a consistent structure for sorting, they are working on the critical task of determining the boundaries of what is and is not included in a category. The fact that real-world data are "messy" and have many attributes makes this task quite complex!

It is important for students to have opportunities to sort real and "messy" data, using their own categories. Too often in the primary classroom, data collection and representation are tied to predetermined categories, usually defined by the teacher before the data are collected. When this happens, students are limited to choosing between the teacher's categories and don't get their own experience in defining them. While this simplifies the task, it also precludes the important mathematical work of considering how and why certain data go together. For example, in **Dialogue Box:** Is a Peach Dessert or Not?, page 143, one kindergartener makes a distinction between *sweet* desserts (cookies, brownies) and *fruit* desserts (apples, grapes). While this organization is clear and understandable to that student, it is confusing to a classmate who points out that his peach was also sweet. Having a clear and convincing definition is a critical part of mathematical communication.

Involving students in making decisions about how things go together brings them into some of the most important aspects of data collection. Only through sorting the actual data they have collected can students arrive at categories that have meaning. In the process, even the youngest students encounter an important idea in data analysis—that different ways of defining and sorting data make different aspects of the data more obvious and salient. This understanding is basic to research in social science and biology as well as mathematics.

"Do You Like . . . ?" Survey Questions

During this data investigation, students work primarily with survey questions that have a yes or no response. Working with only two categories of data can help students see the part-whole relationship between the numbers for each response and the total number of students they have surveyed.

"Do you like" questions are reasonably easy for kindergarteners to generate, and they usually result in answers of yes or no. Students are generally eager to find out whether classmates like or do not like the same things that they do. However, there are some ambiguities that students will need to address concerning situations when their classmates come up with answers other than yes or no.

Even a straightforward question such as "Do you like carrots?" elicited responses other than yes or no in one class. For some students, the answer depended on whether the carrots were raw or cooked, so their response was "sometimes." In another class, a student asked a classmate about a recent movie, and the classmate had not seen the movie. The questioner in this case checked off "yes" after the student's name, assuring the student, "I'm sure you'd love it if you saw it!" (The teacher suggested to this student that he think about whether he needed another category.)

Students are often able to deal with such responses by inventing new categories or recording and keeping track of different responses. We have noticed that after several experiences with surveys, many students begin to plan in advance for alternative responses to their questions.

We recommend that students be encouraged to make their own decisions about responses other than yes or no. Support the student who is trying to decide what to do with unexpected responses by asking if there is a way of labeling these alternative responses, putting them together in a category, or listing them in a separate place.

Be aware that sensitive issues may be raised by questions involving material possessions or opportunities that not all students have. Encourage students to ask questions about things that most people have experience with (e.g., "Do you like meat?" rather than "Do you like Cornish game hens?"). Sensitive issues may also arise with questions about people, including classmates and teachers. You might let students know in advance that they cannot ask questions about liking particular people. Alternatively, you might simply address this only if it comes up.

Teacher Note

Examining Students' Records of Survey Responses

When kindergarteners have the opportunity to participate actively in data collection, they are likely to choose questions and topics that have meaning and relevance to their own lives. Despite this involvement, it takes time for young students to adopt many of the protocols of data collection, such as creating a logical way to keep track of all of the pieces of data they collect and representing the information in an organized way.

When students are first involved in collecting data on their own, it is important to allow them to proceed in a way that makes sense to them. We have found that most kindergarteners are engaged first by the process of collecting data—preparing the survey sheet, interviewing classmates, and recording responses. Data collection starts as a primarily social experience for them, and issues such as making sure to collect data from every student in the class are not of much concern. Many teachers have found that as students gain experience, they begin to see the need for accuracy and consistency in data collection. As this happens, students begin to make better use of tools and strategies that improve accuracy in both collecting and representing the data.

The three examples that follow demonstrate how these kindergarteners kept track of the data they were collecting for their "Do You Like" surveys.

Tammy chose her question, "Do You Like Soccer?" because she is on a soccer team. As she collected data from her classmates, she recorded the name of each person and yes or no to indicate that person's response. Tammy is beginning to understand the need to record her respondents and the information she collects from them, although she has not yet developed a systematic way of keeping track of whom she has asked and whom she still needs to ask.

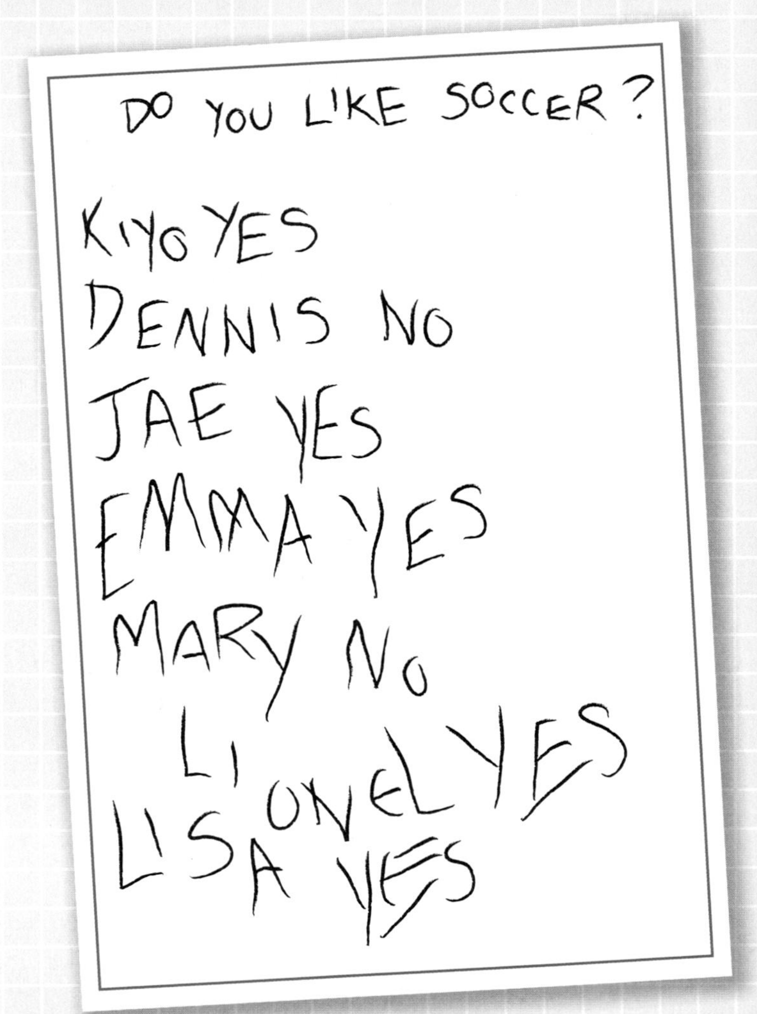

Tammy's Work

Raul's question, "Do You Like Hamsters?" interested him because he had just added two hamsters to his pet collection. Raul has grouped like responses and recorded his data in a way that enables him to compare the two groups directly (although it looks as though he may have stopped collecting data when he ran out of space). Raul, like Tammy, has yet to think of an effective way to keep track of who still has not been interviewed.

Raul's Work

Latoya's representation shows a great deal of information and reflects a purposeful use of data collection. Latoya was interested in finding out how many of her classmates liked invented spelling, a practice that she herself was not fond of. She hoped that if she could show that enough of her classmates felt as she did, invented spelling would no longer be used in her classroom. Latoya arranged her data in a relatively traditional bar graph. She used inch graph paper to organize the information into three columns for the categories Yes, No, and Maybe ["MABE"]. However, the data cannot be compared directly across the columns because some responses have been crossed out. Like Tammy and Raul, Latoya did not collect data from every student in the class, but she does show evidence of understanding the importance of recording and organizing the data she has collected.

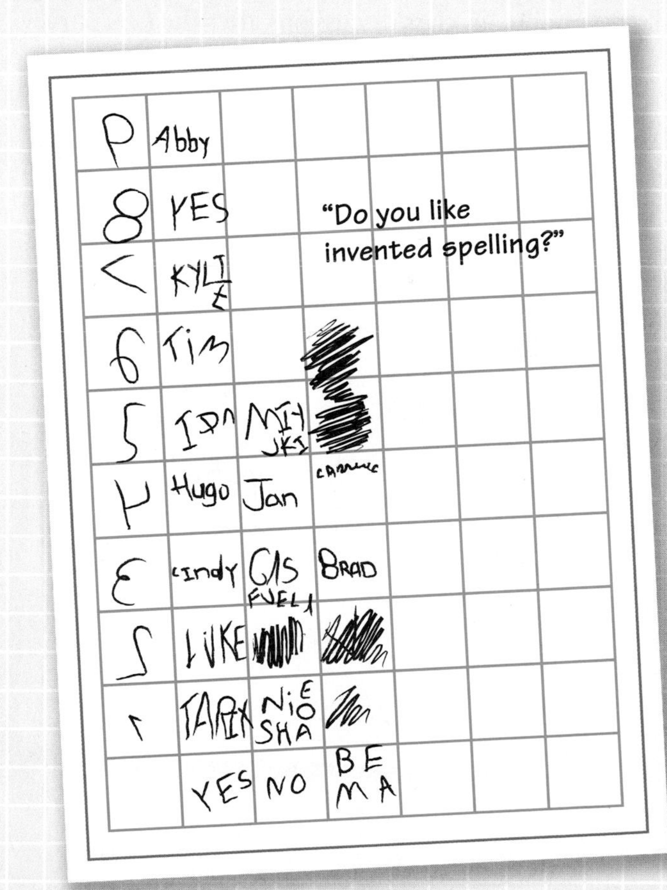

Latoya's Work

In another class, the teacher decided that everyone would use *Student Activity Book* page 77 for collecting data. The format was familiar since the students had been using it as part of the Classroom Routine *Today's Question.* The teacher focused this data collection project on the vegetable garden that the class was planting. Lionel and Elizabeth each collected data about whether students liked carrots. They were able to record responses in the appropriate sections and to count the total number of people in each category. It was interesting to the teacher that few students seemed concerned about whether they had polled everyone in the class (although Lionel came close, surveying 17 out of 20) or about the fact that some students (like Lionel and Elizabeth) asked the same question and got different results. Knowing there would be many more opportunities to talk about data collection, the teacher made a plan to visit these points in class discussions after the next survey.

Do you like ________?

YES	NO
LINDZAY KATIE JULIANA ZHAND Ellen JAKE 6	YUKO MATTHEW 2

Elizabeth's Work

Do you like CAROT'Z?

YES	NO
MARK JARE KRISTINA CAROLINE MARIEL ZIMAIR DANIEL (14) MALIA ELLEN KATIE CIGMAJY ALEXANDIR LINDZAY NAMAH	AMINI MATTHEW YUKO (3)

Lionel's Work

Collecting, recording, and representing data are important aspects of every experience with data. While we can offer students tools and strategies for doing each of these things, we cannot assume that our offerings are useful until the students have had numerous experiences with the process of data collection. It is only with these experiences, guided by the teacher, that students will consider why it is important to collect data from everyone or to organize data so that the results can be easily understood. And only when students work with these issues themselves will they find practical and meaningful ways to use the tools and strategies they are offered.

Teacher Note

Assessing Students as They Use Data to Solve Problems

By the end of this unit, students are expected to be able to use data to solve a problem (Benchmark 2). This means that they identify data to use to solve a problem, accurately solve the problem, and explain or show how they solved the problem. Assessment Checklist: Using Data to Solve Problems (M3) is included to help you keep track of your observations of students' work on this benchmark over the course of the investigations and the unit. What follows is a vignette from one teacher, describing what she learned about students as she observed their work during the activity in Session 3.4.

I chose to present this activity to my students on a day when six students were absent. The attendance problem I posed was somewhat familiar, in that every day during our morning class meeting, we discuss whose names we should place on the absent list that is submitted to the school office. The number of students in the classroom was firmly established; 24 was an important number to these students. On this day, we quickly determined that six students were absent. But what really surprised me was the range of responses to my question, "How many people do you think are here today?" The students' answers ranged from 10 to 22.

Most of my students were immediately interested in "proving" how many students were present today. They chose from materials that I had set out on a table, and most settled into making a representation of their strategy. Although I usually have students work on math problems during our morning Choice Time period, I decided to rearrange our schedule that day to allow time for everyone to work on the same problem. I was most interested in observing the ideas that the students had for solving a somewhat complicated problem.

Kiyo's idea was to make a tower of 24 cubes. "This", she said, "is when all of us are in school." She then took off six cubes, explaining, "because these are the people who are sick. So if I count all of these *cubes (the larger tower), that will be the people who are here today. I counted them before and it was 18." A number of other students used or attempted to use a strategy similar to Kiyo's, but not all had as clear an understanding of what each group or number represented, and not all were successful in counting out 24 cubes.*

Jason decided to give every student in the class a button. He then collected and counted all of the buttons. "If everyone here takes one button, then I can count the buttons and that will tell me how many people are in school because one button, one person!"

Jason's Work

Lisa made a chart with 24 stick figures to represent the 24 kids in our class. She then circled six of these figures and wrote "NT HER" (not here). She explained that if she counted the rest of the stick figures, that would be the number of students in school today. Lisa's strategy was similar to Kiyo's, but she perhaps drew stick figures because they are a more direct representation of the students in the class than cubes are.

Lisa's Work

Brad wrote out the numbers from 1 to 24 to show the kids in the class. Then he crossed off six numbers: 24, 23, 22, 21, 20, 19. "This number here," he said, pointing to 18, "is who is left at school. I can count the numbers, or I see that the last number not crossed off is 18, so that's how many people are in school." Brad's method gave him a concrete way of keeping track. In addition, it provided a visual picture of the count.

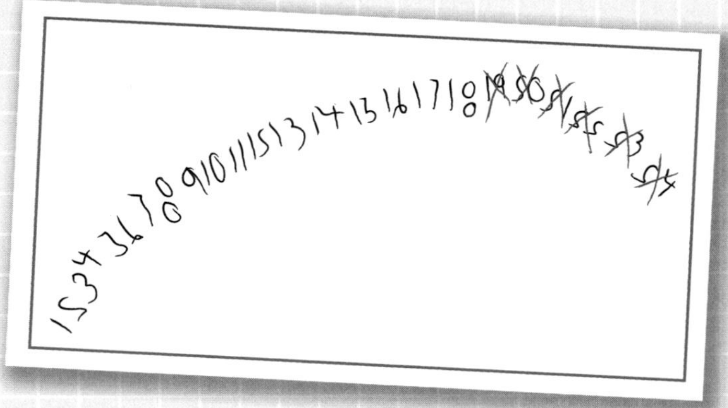

Brad's Work

Sarah's process was similar to Kiyo's, although she used keys from our counting box rather than cubes to represent the people in our class. What I noted about Sarah's strategy was her explanation during the sharing meeting, which uncovered some difficulties in counting that I had not noticed before. As she was demonstrating to her classmates that she used 24 keys to show the 24 students in the class, she counted the keys inaccurately three times, each time losing track of the count at around 16. Eventually, with the help of a classmate, Sarah successfully counted the 24 keys.

What interested me was that Sarah's explanation clearly suggested that she had understood the problem and her strategy for solving it. Until she shared her work, I had not seen her difficulty with counting a set of objects. I questioned whether she was able to hold onto larger amounts and whether the bulkiness of the keys as counters made the counting task more difficult.

Russell was the only student who added to the number of people absent as a way of figuring out the number of people present. He first built a tower of six red interlocking cubes and then snapped together a long tower of blue cubes. "These," he said, "are the people here today because blue is my favorite color. I'll count them until I get to 24. See, 1, 2, 3, 4 . . ." He counted the red cubes to 6 first, and then counted on, using the blue cubes, all the way from 7 to 24.

My question to Russell was, "So how many people are here today?"

"This many," he replied, holding up the tower of blue cubes.

When I asked, "How many is that?" he shrugged his shoulders. "Is there a way you could figure that out?" I asked.

Russell said he could count them, and he did so, beginning with 1, touching each blue cube as he said the next number, arriving at 18. "There are 18 blues," he announced.

"So what does that tell you?" I asked.

"Um, how many people are here today?" Russell still didn't seem entirely sure of what he had just counted.

Many students in the classroom chose to solve the problem using a strategy similar to Kiyo's and Sarah's, but counting out 24 objects to represent the total number of people was challenging. All could accurately take away six objects from the group, but their results varied because they didn't all start out with 24.

During sharing, a few students recognized that they had used similar strategies but arrived at different answers. Some of them were eager to change their representations, while others did not seem to care. In thinking more about this, I decided that the strength of this activity was giving these five- and six-year-olds an opportunity to solve a real-world problem based on data that were familiar and meaningful to them.

Observing students as they solve the problem How Many Are Here Today? can reveal information not only about students' understanding of data and data collection, but also about their ability to make sense of a problem, find strategies for solving a problem, count larger quantities, and show how they solved a problem. As demonstrated above, looking at students' work on this problem can be useful in learning more about the students' understanding, but does not provide the whole picture of their ability to use data to solve a problem. It is important to observe students and ask them about their strategies in order to fully understand how they solved the problem, what they are making sense of, and what they are still working on.

Dialogue Box

Why Do We Need to Know?

Before making representations of the number of students in the class, these students discuss when it is useful to know the number of students in the class.

Teacher: Can you think of some times when people need to know how many of us there are?

Tammy: Maybe they need it for a certain reason.

Teacher: For a certain reason? Can anyone think of a particular reason?

Timothy: They need to know how many people to get books for.

Teacher: For books?

Timothy: Like reading books.

Victor: Yeah, like when everyone in my group got *A Kiss for Little Bear.*

Teacher: OK. Who can think of another time?

Kaitlyn: In case we're taking a field trip and Lionel got left behind and we didn't know he was missing.

Teacher: Did anyone ever use counting when they were on a trip?

Kiyo: Oh, like when we go on a trip and every time we got on and off the bus we counted off to make sure that we always had the same number.

Brad: And my mom does that all the time.

Teacher: What does she do, Brad?

Brad: Like when we go to the zoo and she goes 1, 2, 3 all the time to make sure we are all there.

Jae: When we have a fire drill, the teachers are always counting us.

Teacher: Yes, fire drills and field trips are important times when I need to know exactly how many of you there are. Can you think of any other times?

Carmen: For sending the attendance to the office.

Sarah: For bringing in snacks so that everyone could have a snack.

Teacher: I remember when Timothy's dad brought in treats for his birthday.

Timothy: I told him how many of us there were. And we brought one for each person. And we brought some extras in case we had a visitor or something.

Hugo: And once we brought in apples, but we just brought in three big bags because we knew there would be extras. There were a lot of apples in each bag.

Teacher: So sometimes it's important to know exactly how many we are so that we have enough of something for each person to have one, and sometimes we don't have to count exactly how many—we can think of an "about" amount.

Brad: Things like snacks and stuff are important for everyone to have one, but sometimes there's things that you can share. Like books or puzzles or blocks.

As students share a variety of reasons why it would be useful to know the number of students in the class, the teacher asks them to explain or clarify their reasons. She also highlights that there are some times when an exact count is needed and other times when an estimate will do.

Dialogue Box

How Many Eyes?

In this discussion, students are considering the question of how many eyes are in their classroom. They share strategies for counting the number of eyes and keeping track of whose eyes they have and have not counted.

Teacher: Suppose we wanted to count how many eyes there are. How could we do that so we would have the exact number of eyes?

Abby: We could look at people and count them. I could go around and say "1, 2, 3, 4," like we do for attendance.

Cindy: You'd have to be careful that you don't poke some person's eye when you counted.

Raul: We could take cubes, like when we counted our noses. Each person could take a cube.

Cindy: It'd be different. You have to take two cubes.

Teacher: Why would each person have to take two cubes?

Cindy: Because we have two eyes!

Abby: I think we should just go around and say "1, 2, 3 . . ."

Kyle: Have each person say their own number. Like I would say "1, 2," for my eyes and Abby would say "3, 4," for her eyes.

Teacher: Suppose we went around the circle and counted each person's eyes. Is there some way that we could keep track of whose eyes we have counted and whose eyes we have not counted?

Jason: We could stand up like we do sometimes for attendance. Then when you count your eyes, you sit down.

Students discuss strategies for counting the number of eyes in the class.

Rebecca: We could close our eyes once the person counted our eyes.

Jason: I think we should just sit down 'cause everyone would end up with their eyes closed, and you might get dizzy and fall over or something.

Teacher: Jason suggested having people sit down, and Rebecca suggested closing your eyes. Once everyone was sitting down, or once everyone had their eyes closed, what would we know then?

Abby: Well, if you had your eyes closed, you wouldn't know when you were finished.

Teacher: I'm not sure I understand.

Abby: You couldn't see, so how would we know when everyone had counted unless you peeked, like this [squinting]? Then you could tell when you were finished.

Teacher: So we would have to know when we were finished counting. Any other ideas?

Raul: If everyone was sitting down, then you would know that you counted everyone's eyes.

Teacher: So these are ways of keeping track. Let's choose one to try and then we can choose another one to double-check our count.

Throughout the year, students in this Kindergarten class have discussed ways to count a set of objects and keep track of the count. Each situation presents new challenges for counting and keeping track. In this situation, people's eyes are being counted; this is different from counting a group of objects which can be moved after being counted. Students come up with two strategies for keeping track: people sitting down or closing their eyes when they have been counted. The teacher highlights the purpose of these strategies by asking what they will know once everyone has sat down or closed his or her eyes.

As students count eyes, they are beginning to explore two-to-one correspondence, a challenging idea for kindergarteners. When students observe that counting eyes is different from counting noses because each person has two eyes and everyone will say two numbers while counting eyes, it suggests that these students are noticing a two-to-one relationship between eyes and people. More students will begin to recognize and develop a greater understanding of this relationship as they have more experiences with objects that come in groups in first and second grade. See **Teacher Note,** One-to-One and Two-to-One Correspondence, pages 126–127, for more information.

Dialogue Box

How Are These Coats the Same and Different?

As part of students' work on sorting objects by attributes, they compare the attributes of two objects by discussing how they are the same and how they are different. The teacher in this class has chosen two coats to compare. As students share their ideas about how the coats are the same and how they are different, she records their ideas on a chart.

Teacher: I have brought in two coats today for us to compare. One is my daughter's raincoat, and the other is my winter coat. Please look carefully at these two coats. How are they the same?

Mitchell: The coats aren't the same. They're different coats.

Teacher: You're right, Mitchell. The coats aren't exactly the same, but there are some things that are the same about them. Is there anything you notice is the same about them?

[Mitchell shakes his head]

Lionel: I do! I do! [He giggles.] They're both coats.

Teacher: That might seem silly, but that is something that is the same about them. They are both coats. I am going to write that down under SAME. Anything else?

[There is silence.]

Brad: Well . . . they both have sleeves.

Mitchell: They have TWO sleeves.

Mia: It would be funny if they had five sleeves!

Teacher: That is something the same about them. They both have sleeves. Mitchell, you did notice something that is the same about them. They both have TWO sleeves. [The teacher writes "two sleeves" under SAME.]

Cindy: Look! They both have pockets.

Lionel: But the raincoat has one pocket and the other one has two pockets, so that's not the same.

Cindy: But they both have pockets.

Teacher: Is there a way we could show that on the chart? That they both have pockets, but one coat has one pocket and the other has two.

Beth: Write "pockets" under same and "one and two pockets" under different.

[The teacher writes down what Beth says.]

Rebecca: I see lots of things that are different.

Teacher: Okay, let's talk about what is different about these two coats.

Rebecca: One is yellow and one is gray and one has . . .

Teacher: Let's write that one down first. That's a big one. They are different colors. Let's see if someone else notices something that is different about these two coats.

Yoshio: This one zips and that one doesn't.

Manuel: The big one has buttons.

Teacher: So one has a zipper and the other one has buttons. That's different. I heard Manuel describe my coat as big . . .

Cindy: One is big and one is little! Because you are big and your daughter is little.

Jennifer: And a hood. Your daughter's has a hood and yours doesn't because kids wear hoods and adults wear hats.

Tammy: My mom wears a hood.

Teacher: Well, that is something that is different about these two coats. One has a hood and one doesn't. There is a lot that is different about these two coats, and there might be other things we haven't thought of. Let's look at our list of attributes that are the same and attributes that are different. What attributes did we compare? . . . I noticed we compared sizes of coats. What else?

Sarah: We talked about colors and hoods.

Beth: And zippers and buttons.

Jae: And don't forget sleeves.

As this discussion begins, one student has difficulty seeing how the coats could have anything in common. This is not unusual for young students who may find it hard to identify single attributes of an object and instead only notice the overall look of an object. As the students search for ways the two coats are the same and different, they begin to look closely at the specific attributes of each of them. At the end of the discussion the teacher asks the students to identify the attributes they have been comparing: size, color, hoods, and sleeves. On a different day, the teacher brings in other coats and asks students to use the similarities and differences they identified in this discussion to sort all of the coats. For example, "We said that my coat had buttons. Can we find all of the coats with buttons?"

Being able to identify attributes is an essential part of sorting and classifying objects. Students will need to identify attributes as they sort and classify data and in their work with geometry.

Dialogue Box

Is a Peach Dessert or Not?

In this discussion, students are talking about ways of organizing their favorite lunch foods. Although the categories that students suggest leave many possibilities for overlapping, the teacher is careful not to impose groupings, instead allowing students to make their own decisions about how the lunch data go together.

Mia: I think the pizza people should all be together. That's me and Jennifer and Lionel.

Kaitlyn: Some people liked the same things, like cookies. We should be in a group, too.

Jason: I like my dessert the best, and today it was a brownie. So I could go in the cookie group, too.

Teacher: Can you say why you think your brownie goes with the cookie group?

Jason: Well, it's sort of like a cookie. Sometimes I have cookies for dessert, too.

Teacher: Is there a way to describe foods like cookies and brownies?

Kyle: We could say sweet things.

Russell: They're all things you have for dessert.

Lisa: And they're things I like! We could say it's things you like.

Rebecca: I think we should call it dessert.

Teacher: I've heard a few suggestions for types of groups. Mia suggested the PIZZA group and a couple of people suggested a DESSERT group. Let's start some groups. The people who think they belong to the PIZZA group, sit over here next to the bookshelf. The people who think they belong in the DESSERT group, come sit by the game shelf.

Kyle: I think we should have a sweet group, too.

Yoshio: I had a peach as my favorite thing, but it's not the same kind of dessert as cookies.

Hugo: I think I go with Yoshio. I have an apple and that's fruit.

Rebecca: We should have a fruit dessert group and a sweet dessert group.

Yoshio: A peach is more like an apple than it's like a cookie, so I'll go in the fruit desserts.

Teacher: Kyle, you had the idea for a SWEET group. How does this sound to you?

Kyle: Well, I had peanut butter and fluff as my favorite and it's sort of sweet, but I think I go with Timothy. He has peanut butter, too.

Teacher: You have lots of interesting ideas about how things go together. Let's add the FRUIT DESSERT group and the PEANUT BUTTER group. Then we can see which people go where, and who is left.

The teacher asks the students to come up with their own categories, but guides the discussion by asking students to explain their decisions about where they think their foods belong and by asking them to describe the common attributes among foods they decide go together in order to name the groups. The students in this class begin categorizing their favorite foods from their lunches by putting together the foods that are exactly the same: a pizza group and a cookie group. They then begin to think about more general groups—sweet groups or dessert groups. As they define their groups, students find that not every food fits easily into the groups they have chosen. For example, does a peach go into the dessert group or not? It is dessert, but not the same as cookies or brownies. Peanut butter and fluff is sweet, but it also goes with another peanut butter lunch. Students may go on to rearrange their favorite foods from their lunches in a number of different ways, continue to make new groups, or put groups together to try to accommodate all of the data.

Dialogue Box

Will All Our Seeds Germinate?

One Kindergarten teacher decided to do an activity similar to the "Do You Like . . . ?" surveys in her science curriculum. The issues students faced concerning categorizing responses other than yes or no are similar to the ones students encounter in the "Do You Like . . . ?" surveys investigation.

Each spring this class plants sunflower seeds, which are then transplanted to a local farm. In the fall, when students return as first graders, they harvest the sunflowers for the seeds.

In this activity, the teacher is working with a group of six students. They are planning to survey the class about whether they think their sunflower seeds will germinate. The students become very involved in a discussion about the possible responses to the question "Will all our seeds germinate?"

Russell: Well, maybe half will grow and half won't.

Mary: I think more than half. I think just three won't germinate.

Teacher: If we were going to make a survey question about our seeds, what would we need to do?

Sarah: We need lines on the paper and then you put down the words and then you write down *Yes, No,* and *I'm not sure.*

Teacher: *Yes, No,* and *I'm not sure*—do these answers work for this question?

Sarah: You could say *"Yes, they will all grow," "No, they won't,"* and *"I'm not sure if they will."* So they work.

Brad: I think you could put *A lot, A little,* or *Not at all.*

Russell: What if you say *"I think half will germinate"*? Then you should have *Yes, No, I'm not sure,* and *I think half will grow.*

Mary: That's a good idea. We need a ruler to draw lines.

Teacher: So, how should we set up the paper if we are going to make this a class survey question? Where should the lines be?

Mary: Like this. [She uses a ruler to show how she would draw vertical lines on the paper to divide it into four response columns.]

Sarah: But my name is too long to go in that space. When I write it, it might bump into the name on the next space. It should be bigger.

Mary: We could leave out *I'm not sure.* It's like *No.*

Teacher: Are they the same thing?

Ricardo: *No* means that's your answer. It's different from *I'm not sure* because *I'm not sure* means you aren't sure.

Jae: *I'm not sure* and *Half will grow* is the same.

Ricardo: No, *Half will grow* means "I think half the seeds will grow." That's not like *I'm not sure.*

Brad: I think if we don't put *I'm not sure,* then Jack will pick something else. He always picks *I'm not sure.*

Mary: We could not use *I'm not sure* but instead use *Maybe.*

Russell: If we just put *Yes* and *No,* we can just put the line in the middle.

Sarah: But what if you're not sure?

Teacher: At first I thought we would all work on the same kind of chart, but should we each make a different one?

Mary: Do *Maybe.*

Teacher: Is *Maybe* the same thing as *I'm not sure?*

Sarah: No.

Jae: Both mean *I'm not sure.*

Brad: Yeah, that's right.

Teacher: I'm going to get more paper so that you each can design your own survey chart.

Sarah: But *Maybe* is not the same.

Teacher: Since each of you is going to design your own survey, you can choose to include *I'm not sure* as one of your choices, Sarah.

After this discussion, the students decided for themselves how many responses to allow for. Some of their survey charts are shown below.

As students discuss the seemingly simple possible responses to their survey question (yes or no), they realize that there are some other different possible responses as well. As they design their recording sheet for responses, they think about how to address some important issues in collecting and recording data, including how to accommodate all possible responses while recording the data in a manageable fashion. Because the students are not able to agree on what to include on the recording sheet, the teacher decides to let the students design their own.

Sample Student Work

Student Math Handbook

The *Student Math Handbook Flip Chart* pages related to this unit are pictured on the following pages. This book is designed to be used flexibly: as a resource for providing visual prompts for the teacher to use when introducing a new math activity or idea, as a resource for reviewing math words and ideas with students, and as a resource for students to use as they are doing classwork.

Math Words and Ideas | Read Together

More Counting

How many students are here today?

1 2 3 4 5 6 7 8 9 10 11 12 13 14 15 16 17 18 19 20

20 students are here today.

How many students are in your class?

Note to Teacher: ***Who Is in School Today?* Session 1.1.** Use this page to show that we use numbers both to count a set of objects (1, 2, 3, . . . 20) and to describe the quantity of those objects (the total is 20).

SMH 18 eighteen

Math Words and Ideas, p. 18

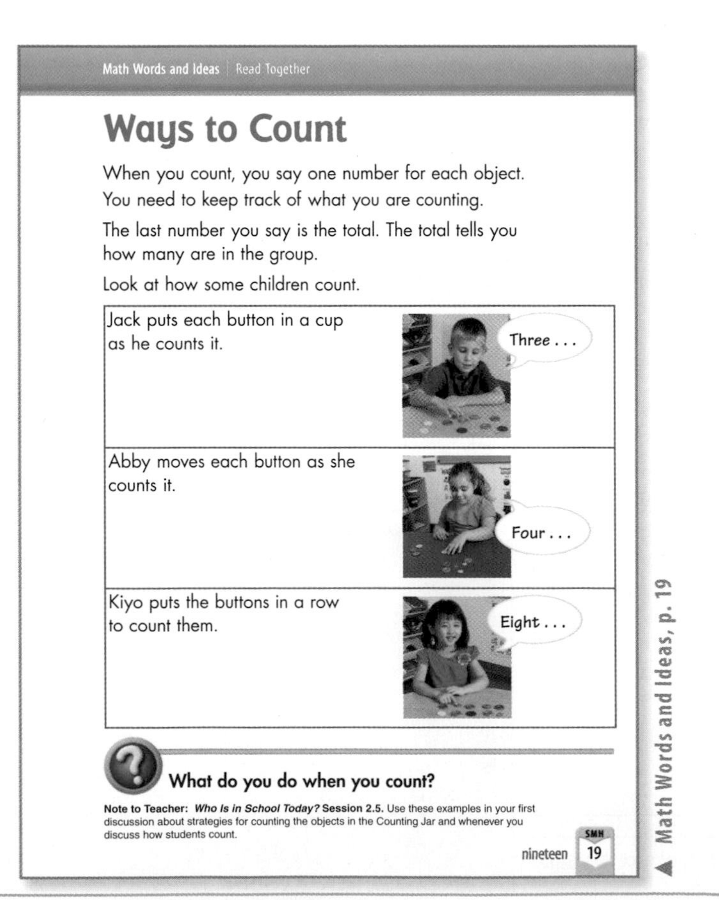

Math Words and Ideas | Read Together

Ways to Count

When you count, you say one number for each object.
You need to keep track of what you are counting.

The last number you say is the total. The total tells you how many are in the group.

Look at how some children count.

Jack puts each button in a cup as he counts it.

Three . . .

Abby moves each button as she counts it.

Four . . .

Kiyo puts the buttons in a row to count them.

Eight . . .

What do you do when you count?

Note to Teacher: ***Who Is in School Today?* Session 2.5.** Use these examples in your first discussion about strategies for counting the objects in the Counting Jar and whenever you discuss how students count.

nineteen SMH 19

Math Words and Ideas, p. 19

Math Words and Ideas | Read Together

Counting Jar

Cubes

Step 1. Count how many.

Step 2. Make the same amount.

Hugo

Beth

Step 3. Show how many.

4

4 cubes

Note to Teacher: ***Who Is in School Today?* Session 2.1.** Encourage students to use this page when they are working on the Counting Jar to help them remember the steps of the activity.

SMH 20 twenty

Math Words and Ideas, p. 20

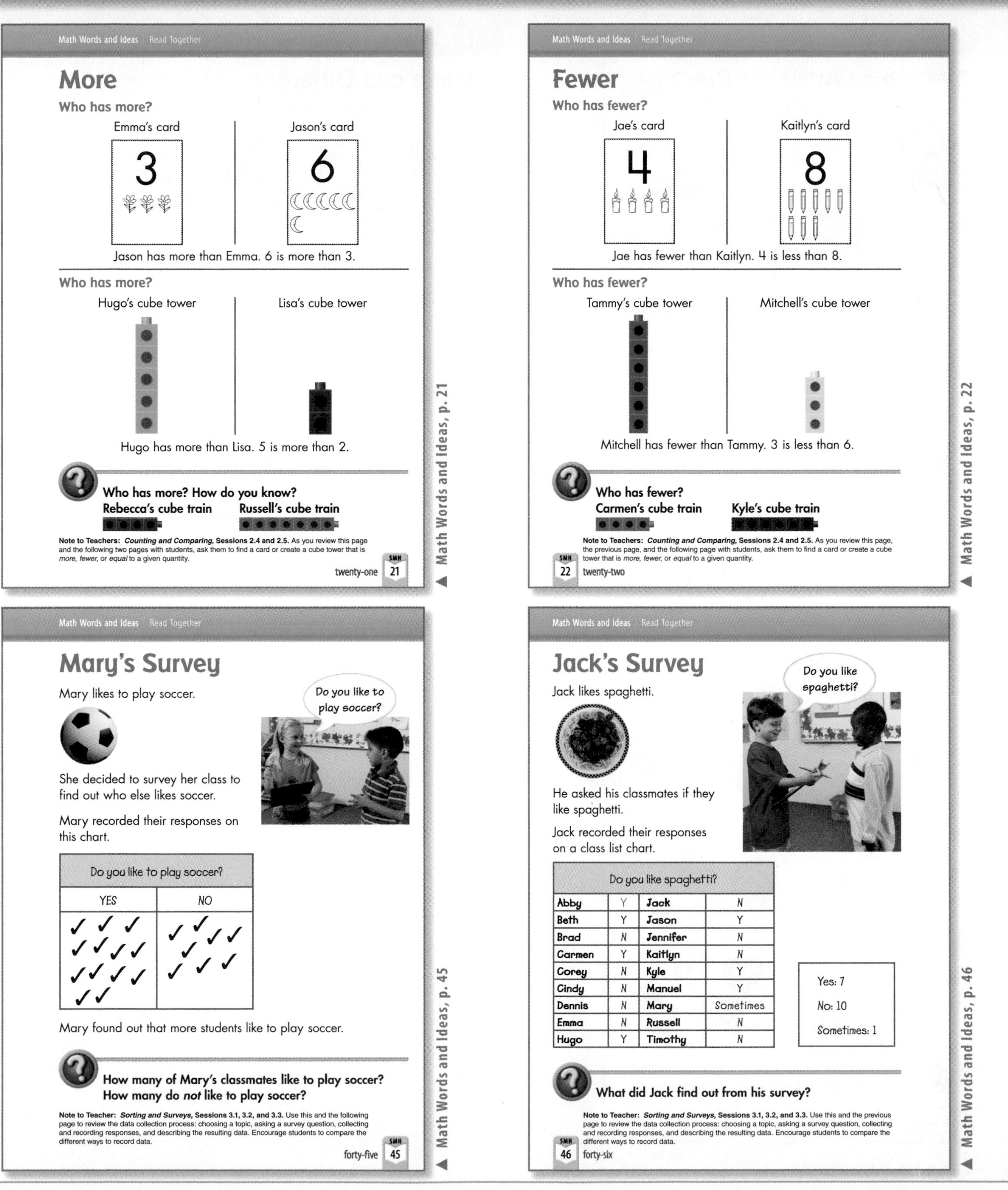

More

Who has more?

Emma's card	Jason's card
3	6

Jason has more than Emma. 6 is more than 3.

Who has more?

Hugo's cube tower | Lisa's cube tower

Hugo has more than Lisa. 5 is more than 2.

Who has more? How do you know?

Rebecca's cube train | **Russell's cube train**

Note to Teachers: ***Counting and Comparing,*** **Sessions 2.4 and 2.5.** As you review this page and the following two pages with students, ask them to find a card or create a cube tower that is *more, fewer,* or *equal* to a given quantity.

Math Words and Ideas, p. 21

Fewer

Who has fewer?

Jae's card	Kaitlyn's card
4	8

Jae has fewer than Kaitlyn. 4 is less than 8.

Who has fewer?

Tammy's cube tower | Mitchell's cube tower

Mitchell has fewer than Tammy. 3 is less than 6.

Who has fewer?

Carmen's cube train | **Kyle's cube train**

Note to Teachers: ***Counting and Comparing,*** **Sessions 2.4 and 2.5.** As you review this page, the previous page, and the following page with students, ask them to find a card or create a cube tower that is *more, fewer,* or *equal* to a given quantity.

Math Words and Ideas, p. 22

Mary's Survey

Mary likes to play soccer.

She decided to survey her class to find out who else likes soccer.

Mary recorded their responses on this chart.

Do you like to play soccer?	
YES	NO
✓✓✓✓✓✓✓✓✓✓✓✓✓	✓✓✓✓✓✓✓✓

Mary found out that more students like to play soccer.

How many of Mary's classmates like to play soccer?
How many do *not* like to play soccer?

Note to Teacher: ***Sorting and Surveys,*** **Sessions 3.1, 3.2, and 3.3.** Use this and the following page to review the data collection process: choosing a topic, asking a survey question, collecting and recording responses, and describing the resulting data. Encourage students to compare the different ways to record data.

Math Words and Ideas, p. 45

Jack's Survey

Jack likes spaghetti.

He asked his classmates if they like spaghetti.

Jack recorded their responses on a class list chart.

Do you like spaghetti?			
Abby	Y	Jack	N
Beth	Y	Jason	Y
Brad	N	Jennifer	N
Carmen	Y	Kaitlyn	N
Corey	N	Kyle	Y
Cindy	N	Manuel	Y
Dennis	N	Mary	Sometimes
Emma	N	Russell	N
Hugo	Y	Timothy	N

Yes: 7
No: 10
Sometimes: 1

What did Jack find out from his survey?

Note to Teacher: ***Sorting and Surveys,*** **Sessions 3.1, 3.2, and 3.3.** Use this and the previous page to review the data collection process: choosing a topic, asking a survey question, collecting and recording responses, and describing the resulting data. Encourage students to compare the different ways to record data.

Math Words and Ideas, p. 46

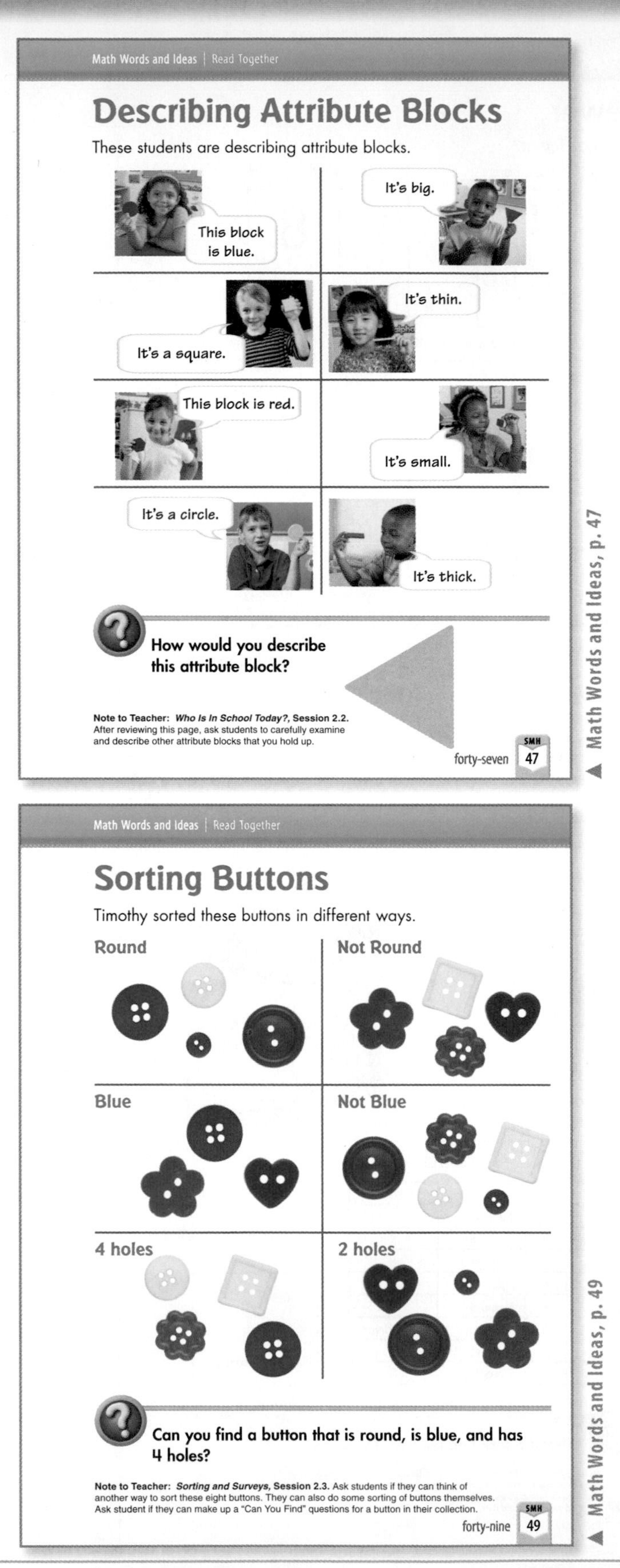

Math Words and Ideas | Read Together

Describing Attribute Blocks

These students are describing attribute blocks.

How would you describe this attribute block?

Note to Teacher: *Who Is In School Today?*, Session 2.2. After reviewing this page, ask students to carefully examine and describe other attribute blocks that you hold up.

forty-seven SMH 47

Math Words and Ideas, p. 47

Math Words and Ideas | Read Together

Sorting Buttons

Timothy sorted these buttons in different ways.

Can you find a button that is round, is blue, and has 4 holes?

Note to Teacher: *Sorting and Surveys*, Session 2.3. Ask students if they can think of another way to sort these eight buttons. They can also do some sorting of buttons themselves. Ask student if they can make up a "Can You Find" questions for a button in their collection.

forty-nine SMH 49

Math Words and Ideas, p. 49

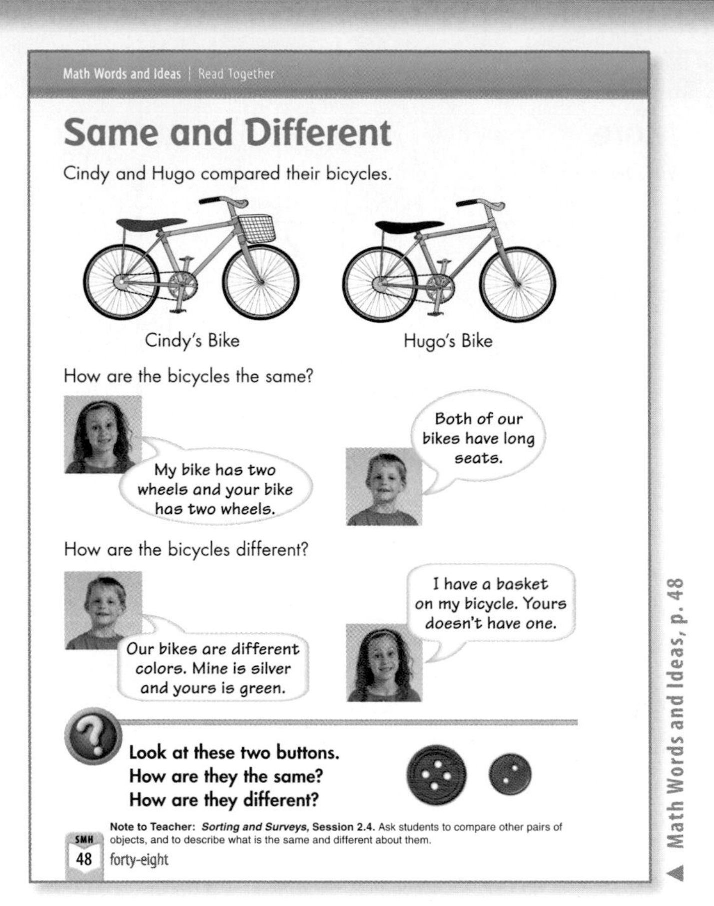

Math Words and Ideas | Read Together

Same and Different

Cindy and Hugo compared their bicycles.

How are the bicycles the same?

How are the bicycles different?

Look at these two buttons. How are they the same? How are they different?

Note to Teacher: *Sorting and Surveys*, Session 2.4. Ask students to compare other pairs of objects, and to describe what is the same and different about them.

SMH 48 forty-eight

Math Words and Ideas, p. 48

Index

IN THIS UNIT

G

I

M

N

O

P

R

S

T